Extended Youth

Extended Youth

THE PROMISE OF GERONTOLOGY

by Robert W. Prehoda

FOREWORD BY JOHN H. NORTHROP

G. P. PUTNAM'S SONS

New York

Copyright © 1968 by Robert W. Prehoda

*Library of Congress Catalog
Card Number: 68-15519*

*This book is dedicated to
my golden girls*

STACY and MARLA

*who are growing up into the
exciting future of
extended youth*

Preface

EXTENDED youth, the promise of gerontology, analyzes the major theories that explain senescence—the process of aging which is characterized by physical and mental decline in its later stages. The primary purpose of this book is to inform both scientists and intelligent laymen of what may be expected in the extension of the life-span—if sufficient efforts and funds are devoted to refining therapies that will modify the aging process itself.

Information for this book has been obtained through conventional scholarship and extensive travel. In addition to references in the bibliography, many other books, uncounted scientific journals and articles in popular publications have been reviewed. I have visited the laboratories of many scientists investigating various aspects of biological senescence in the United States, England, Western Europe and the Soviet Union. These trips have permitted discussions with most of the leading scientists working at the frontiers of aging research. This data (supplemented by extensive correspondence) has convinced me that a full understanding of the causes of senescence is now emerging. The history of science clearly indicates that practical applications or control of natural phenomena are possible soon after contending theories can be placed in proper perspective, which is now happening in the study of biological aging.

The reader will note that most of the references in this book are made to research underway in the Anglo-American scientific community (Australia, Canada, England and the United States). This does not imply that all the primary efforts to control aging are centered in these countries. Equally imaginative research is underway in many other countries including Japan and the Soviet Union. Scientists everywhere appear to have reached the same basic conclusions.

This book is also intended to convince readers that a greatly expanded research program directed toward the control of aging is justified by contemporary scientific evidence. I have reviewed primarily the pattern of aging research funding neglect in the United States (Chapter 16), because I am most familiar with detailed R&D expenditures in my own country. However, scientists in England, the Soviet Union and other countries have informed me that their funding problems are similar to those faced by their American counterparts. Therefore the message is equally applicable to the people of every nation with an advanced capability in biological research.

It is my hope that this anaysis will play an active part in alerting scientists and laymen in many countries to the need for a greater scientific effort to achieve practical therapies that will permit the age of extended youth to begin before the advent of the twenty-first century.

ROBERT W. PREHODA

Encino, California
May, 1968

Acknowledgments

I PARTICULARLY appreciate the understanding with which Dr. John H. Northrop introduces my analysis of the prospect for extended youth in his insightful Foreword to this book.

My extensive discussions of the foreseeable impact of longevity with my good friend the late Dandridge M. Cole are gratefully remembered.

The pioneering genius of Dr. Christiaan Barnard serves as an inspiration to all scientists seeking to extend the active portion of man's life.

Many specialists in diverse disciplines have supplied useful information and have reviewed portions of this book in various draft stages. They are in no way responsible for the use I have made of their suggestions, and acknowledgment of their assistance does not imply that they agree with all the conclusions or recommendations in this book. They include: Dr. B. Renault Able, Fred A. Andrews, Dr. O. A. Battista, Donald K. Bjelke, Dr. Johan Bjorksten, Andrew Bluemle, Ronald S. Burke, Clark T. Cameron, Dale L. Carpenter, Dr. Donald G. Carpenter, Arthur C. Clarke, Dr. Eugene L. Colichman, Dr. Alex Comfort, Dr. Howard J. Curtis, Dr. Stephen H. Dole, Theodore J. Gordon, Dr. Denham Harman, Dr. Eugene G. Jussek, Herman Kahn, Dr. Robert R. Kohn, Dr. John M. Lagerwerff, Dr. Bernard LaSalle, Dr. Choh Hao Li, the late Dr. Clive M. McCay and Mrs. Jeanette B. McCay, Patrick M. McGrady, Jr., Dr. John G. Meitner, Hasan Ozbekhan, Dr. Linus Pauling, Neil P. Ruzic, Dr. Hans Selye, Leo J. Skubic, Dr. Harry Soble, Dr. Joseph W. Still, G. Harry Stine, Dr. Henry Swan II, William Targ, Sir George Thomson, Dr. Frederic Verzár, Dr. Roy L. Walford, Dr. Stephen Zamenhof, and Claudette.

Contents

Foreword

MANY infectious diseases of the young and middle-aged have been controlled and almost eliminated as a result of two fundamental discoveries ("Hahn-Strassman points" in the Prehoda lexicon): (1) Pasteur's discovery of the bacterial origin of many infectious diseases and (2) the discovery of the antibotics by Fleming, Chain, and Florey.

As a result, the expectation of life of those under 70 has been greatly increased over the last 100 years. In contrast, the expectation of life of those over 70 or 75 remains about the same as it was when vital statistics were first accumulated and phlebotomy was common practice.

In spite of this fact the study of senescence and of the duration of life is noticeable principally for its neglect. The amount of money spent on research in this field is minute compared to that spent on defense or space projects. The obvious conclusion is that we are more interested in reaching the moon, or in shortening the lives of our enemies, than we are in prolonging our own lives.

One reason for this strange neglect of gerontology may be the lack of faith in the success of such research, as though the problem of duration of life was essentially insoluble, comparable to the invention of a perpetual motion machine or an antigravity device. This pessimistic conclusion is by no means inescapable. In fact, a poll of the scientific community 50 years or more ago as to the probability of discovering the philosopher's stone or the elixir of life, would have elicited the information that discovery of the philosopher's stone was theoretically impossible, while that of the life was simply improbable. The philosopher's stone, which can transmute the elements, is now in everyday use, while the elixir of life is still elusive. There is plenty of evidence, however, that the difficulties of the search are more practical than theoretical.

Living cells are potentially immortal as shown by the fact that plant grafts and cultures of microorganisms or cells live indefinitely, provided they are kept growing. Redwood trees live thousands of years and even men have lived over 100 years. Increasing the length of life to 100 or more, therefore, does not entail any radical new theory or practice, but simply the knowledge of how this has been done.

The fact that evolution has, in general, led to short-lived species may simply be because short-lived individuals are a more efficient way for the preservation of the species than long-lived ones, owing to the chance of accidental death or injury. Who would labor to produce a car which could run for 100 million miles, if the chances were that it would be wrecked in less than 1 million? It may be significant that long-lived species, the redwoods or giant tortoises, are almost accident-proof, or at least they were so before the advent of Homo sapiens.

Part of the puzzle is known: Aging does not begin until growth stops. The next question is: What injures and eventually kills nongrowing cells? The answer may be the inactivation of essential molecules by cross-linkage, as Johan Bjorksten has emphasized. There is considerable experimental evidence for the correctness of this hypothesis. The answer to this question may very well cut the Gordian knot so that all that will be left to do is to unravel the loose ends. It would be surprising indeed if no way could be found to circumvent the harmful reactions once they are identified. In any event the problem appears no more difficult of solution than a planetary landing, provided equivalent time and energy were spent on it.

This book of Prehoda's is persuasive evidence for the development of such an attack on the problem of aging, a problem that is of direct personal interest to more and more of us every year. The book is very clear and interesting. The author has escaped both the Scylla of sensational exaggeration and the Charybdis of boring technicalities.

JOHN H. NORTHROP

Extended Youth

1

~~~~~~~~~~~~~~~~~~~~~~~~~~~~

Overview of Aging

THE life-span of man, theoretically, may be unlimited since the body is a self-repairing organism. Some scientists have suggested that the present barrier to a greatly extended life-span is found in the various chemical and biological reactions that take place once the body ceases to grow. These changes cause aging and are the subject of a specialized branch of science known as gerontology. The goals of gerontology are the extension of the human life-span and the assurance of the mental and physical capacity to enjoy longevity.

Senescence * in mammals occurs once the body ceases to grow and is manifested in the organism's diminishing capacity to withstand the environmental stresses to which it is subjected. Although the symptoms are uniform, the rate of aging varies from organism to organism, a phenomenon of great significance to the study of senescence. One pioneer in gerontology, Dr. Nathan W. Shock, observes: [1]

> One key to understanding aging and particularly to taking action that might extend the human life span can be found in the differences in the rate of aging observed in different individuals. These differences indicate that many factors play a role in aging. When we know why some people age less rapidly than others

* Defined in Glossary, pp. 245 to 250.

19

we may be able to create conditions that will minimize the loss of functioning cells and tissues, thereby enabling many more people to live as long as those who live longest today.

Dr. Alex Comfort, a leading gerontologist, at University College in London, says: "If we kept throughout life the same resistance to stress, injury, and disease that we had at the age of ten, about one-half of us here today might expect to survive in 700 years time." [2] There is no evidence that anyone has lived 700 years, so man's maximum life-span to date is far short of this intriguing potential.

The degenerative processes of aging occur whether the organism is subject to disease or not, and are primarily the result of cell losses throughout the body. Progressive loss of body cells is thought to be due to a decline in the body's capacity of self-repair and reproduction. Most men between the ages of 65 and 90 average a 20-pound weight loss. Between 30 and 75, hormone production declines, the kidneys show a 55 percent reduction in efficiency and the speed of nerve impulses along single fibers declines 10 to 15 percent. Muscle strength, maximum breathing capacity and oxygen uptake all diminish by about 50 percent. The average weight of the brain falls from 1,375 grams (3.03 pounds) at the age of 30 to 1,232 grams (2.72) pounds at 90.

At the age of 75, the average heart pumps only 65 percent as much blood as at age 30; the brain receives 80 percent as much blood; the kidney's receive only 42 percent as much. This decrease in blood flow to the kidneys appears to be an adaptive mechanism permitting a greater blood flow to the brain, which is particularly dependent on a good blood supply. Mental senility is largely caused by the physical destruction of brain and nerve tissue due to hardening of blood vessels and small strokes.

The bones tend to lose their calcium salts and become brittle. The connective tissues of the body contract and harden, resulting in the characteristic stoop of old age. Lost cells usually are replaced by connective tissue, which partly accounts for the decreased amount of water in the body as it ages. The skin loses its elasticity and ability to retain water. Layers of fat directly underneath the skin gradually change and are no longer uniform, causing skin shrinking and wrinkles. The arteries harden, thicken, and lose their elasticity.

As a result of all of these losses in reserve capacity, the organism finds it more and more difficult to adjust to changes in its environment. It takes longer to return to normal function after disturbances caused by disease, shock or accident, and the individual finally dies.

Yet, despite the seemingly inescapable statistics of senescence, history and literature record man's persistent hope and search for the "elixir of life," and set forth the exciting examples of those who did live beyond the limits of a pitiably brief life-span.

In ancient times it was believed that air exhaled by young virgins helped to preserve life. Similarly, the practice of "gerocomia" sought to rejuvenate aged men by placing young virgins in their beds, as in the Book of Kings when virgins lay in King David's bed so that the King "may get heat."

Almost all early religions include legends of long-lived ancestors. The Bible, for example, mentions the life-spans of each of the first 10 patriarchs:

Adam	930 years	Jared	962 years
Seth	912 years	Enoch	365 years
Enoch	905 years	Methuselah	969 years
Kenan	910 years	Lamech	777 years
Mahalalel	895 years	Noah	950 years

These Biblical figures who lived before the flood are called "antediluvians" and the term "antediluvian standard" is frequently encountered in older literary references to aging. It is taken from the Book of Genesis in the Bible and refers to a life-span between 700 and 1,000 years. Methuselah's name, of course, has become a byword for exceptional longevity.

Some modern scholars have suggested that in recording

the ages of the legendary patriarchs lunar months were sub-
stituted for years or that the decimal point might have been
shifted. Legends of the antediluvian type are common in all
early mythologies and religions. While scientifically doubtful,
the antediluvian theme does reflect man's historic desire for
an extended life-span.

Stories of long-lived people have continued through the
ages till the present day. Dr. Alexander A. Bogomoletz, in his
book *The Prolongation of Life,* mentions a number of historical
cases of exceptional longevity, though for all of them docu-
mentary evidence is sparse. The best known is the famous
Thomas Parr, frequently referred to as "Old Parr," who is reported to have lived to be 152. He was an English farmer
who was brought to the court of King Charles I by the Earl
of Arundel. The transition from rustic countryside to lusty
court life was too much for Old Parr and he soon died from
overindulgence in food and drink. King Charles' physician,
the great William Harvey, performed an autopsy and reported
that Old Parr's muscles, intestines, and brain were in an excellent state of preservation.

The recorded evidence appears better for a Dane, Christian
Dankenberg, who died of alcoholism in 1772 at the age of 146.
He had lived the rugged life of a sailor, fought against the
Swedes in several wars, was captured by Barbary pirates at
the age of 68, and escaped at 83. He fought the Swedes in
another war before he settled down at 111 and married the
widow of a sea captain. The remainder of Dankenberg's life
was active and lusty.

Other exceptional life-spans mentioned by Bogomoletz include: P. Ktzarzen who died at 185 in 1724 in Austria;
G. Jenkins who died at 169 in 1670 in England; Joseph Gur-
rington who died at 160 in 1797 in Norway; a Hungarian
couple, John and Sara Roven, who lived for 172 and 164
years. Another Hungarian peasant who died in 1905 at age
195 was survived by his 155-year-old son. Elizabeth Durieux

died in 1857 at 140. Bogomoletz also reports a number of modern supercentenarians, most of them peasants from the Caucasus Mountains in Georgia and Axerbaijan. In 1966, an Azerbaijanian named Muslimov was reported to be 161, though it should be remembered that prior to the revolution, peasants used to falsify their ages to escape conscription in the Czar's army.

Some Soviet gerontologists suggest that heredity, sparce diet and the exercise required in a mountain environment all contribute to exceptional longevity, though there is not a high concentration of centenarians in the Alps, the Andes or the Carpathian Mountains.

There are unconfirmed reports of supercentenarians in other parts of the world. The inhabitants of the Hunza valley in the Himalayan mountain region of northern Pakistan are said to live exceptionally long lives. In 1963, a Turkish woman, Hatice Nine, was reported to be 168. Another Turk, Zaro Agha, who died in 1935 was reported to be 160. In 1957 considerable publicity was given to a Columbian Indian, Javier Pereira, who was reported to be 167.

For many other mammals the maximum life-span is about twice the modal (average) age of adult death. If the analogy applies, this would suggest a maximum life-span for man of about 150 years. It is quite possible that there are a handful of living humans who may be between 140 and 150, but it is doubtful that higher reported age levels are correct.

Despite the unreliable records on which these examples are based, such instances of exceptional longevity indicate that aging can occur at a very slow rate. But more important, they suggest that aging is not necessarily inevitable. This dramatic possibility is finding support in even the more conservative scientific circles. The American scientist Dr. Linus Pauling observes: [3]

> Death is unnatural . . . theoretically, man is quite immortal. His body tissues replace themselves. He is a self-repairing machine.

And yet, he gets old and dies, and the reasons for this are still a mystery. When once a real understanding of the physiological activity of chemical substances is obtained, medical progress will be swift. The medical research man will be a molecular architect. He will be able to draw the atomic blueprints for promising pharmacological compounds. Chemists may then synthesize them and biologists test them. He will be able to analyze and interpret the structure of enzymes, tissues and viruses to learn the mechanisms of disease, and then the way of combating diseases. When this time comes—and it is coming —medicine will indeed have become an exact science.

The belief that mammals are subject to a fixed life-span that cannot be significantly extended was disproved over 30 years ago. The late Dr. Clive M. McCay conducted dietary experiments which almost doubled the life-span of rats. The details and implications of McCay's experiments will be examined thoroughly in Chapter 2.

In 1912, Dr. Alexis Carrel took some chicken heart embryo tissue and placed it in a nourishing blood plasma fluid. As the heart tissue grew it was periodically trimmed. It outlived the normal life-span of a chicken many times. Carrel concluded that living cells nourished, washed, and sheltered in a test tube do not decay or die. They continue dividing, suggesting that immortality may be the natural potential of protoplasm (the basic substance of all life). The results of this experiment have been interpreted to indicate that death is not a natural process but the result of disease, stress, or a combination of factors that may yield to research and preventative treatment.

The results of Carrel's classic experiment were not questioned for many years. Recently, however, some investigations have concluded that tissue culture experiments do not offer valid evidence of the potential immortality of protoplasm because such cells exhibit changes that cause them to resemble cancer cells. The debate is still open, but future progress in gerontology may verify Carrel's original conclusion that physical immortality may be part of nature's grand design.

Dr. Albert I. Lansing, a leading gerontologist, conducted experiments with rotifers, tiny circular pond-dwelling animals which reproduce asexually, and usually live about 24 days. Careful observation revealed that rotifers born of older mothers had abnormally short life-spans, and that if daughters of these older mothers were not allowed to breed until they too were older, their offsprings had shorter lives still. Eventually, the life-span of the older-mother line was so short that they could not reproduce and they became extinct. Early death seemed to be the result of unidentified poisons which accumulated in the bodies of mature rotifers that had stopped growing.

Succeeding generations from young growing mothers enjoyed increasingly extended lives, a tendency known as the "Lansing effect." Generations of rotifers continually bred from adolescent mothers eventually lived four times longer than usual, the equivalent of a 280-year human life-span. These findings contain important clues to human aging. They indicate that unknown substances and biochemical reactions exist in nature that are able to postpone senility and death for very long periods. The implications of this conclusion are prophetic. The discovery and control of the basic mechanism which govern the aging process are within the scope of scientific exploration and knowledge.

Until very recently, however, modern medical research has been directed primarily toward the treatment and cure of specific illnesses and diseases, while research into the causes of biological senescence was neglected.

There are two important reasons why this was so. All early medical efforts to extend the human life-span failed, and such efforts became identified with quacks and charlatans. To many scientists the extension of the human life-span was a fundamental impossibility in the class with other fantastic and unrealizable goals of the early alchemists. Few scientists engaged in aging research because of the concern for their professional reputations and because there were no sources of financial support for such research. Many gerontologists had to disguise their proposals on aging as cancer investigations in order to have any chance of funding support.

In the post-World-War-II years, attitudes changed, largely due to the rapid and extensive development of modern science and medical technology. The German wartime advances in rocketry, for example, made it clear that space exploration was possible. The exotic and exciting goals of science suddenly were given a degree of professional respectability. This change in attitude made possible the birth of gerontology in 1950 as a separate branch of science. Almost all of our progress in understanding the causes of aging has occurred since that time.

Yet, despite the credibility now accorded to the methods and goals of gerontology, there is still a serious imbalance in the distribution of federal biomedical research funds, with only 1 or 2 percent allotted to studies of the aging process. The reasons for this imbalance are twofold: These funds are controlled principally by the medical profession, where specialization causes members to be oriented toward study of specific diseases rather than the fundamental biochemical processes which affect resistance to all disease. Secondly, among the general public, and even among physicians, there are many who still believe that senescence is an inescapable evil.

The need for a more total understanding of the aging process becomes increasingly apparent. Even if the three major causes of death in older people—heart disease, strokes and cancer—are found curable, the average human life-span would still not exceed 85 or 90.

The suggestion that curing the major diseases will result in a life-span extension of 10 to 15 years is in itself subject to question. Attempting to determine the potential life-span of man by manipulating death certificate statistics can be very misleading. In the first place, this assessment requires the assumption that the correct cause of death has been written on the death certificate that has become part of the total statistical sample. But autopsies are performed on only a small percentage of people who die of natural causes. Moreover, the future therapies that would cure strokes and heart disease would probably also partly rejuvenate the arterial system, conferring life-extending benefits beyond the elimination of cardiovascular illness.

Nor would the human life-span be extended significantly by replacing diseased organs with artificial prostheses or transplants. The refinement of these approaches to specific diseases is of course among the most exciting contemporary developments in applied science. From a theoretical standpoint it may someday be possible to replace any or all of the body's organs (except the brain) with artificial devices or transplants. However, this approach again only offers cures for specific diseases. The brain and other body tissues would continue to age. In fact, 75 percent of all deaths may be due to the aging process because most illnesses would not be fatal if we could maintain the resistance and ability to heal that is ours at the age of 15.

Any truly significant extension in human life-span must come from an understanding and control of the basic causes of biological aging. Then specific cures, transplants and artificial organs can be used in synergistic association with the anti-aging therapy to enable a higher percentage of people to enjoy the maximum benefits of an extended life-span.

Unless a massive effort is made to understand and control biological aging, contemporary biomedical research will soon reach a point of diminishing returns. The extension of youth should, therefore, be made an official national scientific goal, given Presidential and Congressional endorsement. The dramatic nature of a major national gerontology program would cause our scientists to focus their attention more fully on the aging process. Probably we have already reached the point where the necessary solutions to the conquest of aging exist at various stages of refinement throughout our increasingly complex scientific establishment. The principal problem would be the proper means of bringing together all the specialists who collectively are capable of providing the necessary answers. Dr. Bernard Strehler, a biologist for the gerontology branch of the National Institutes of Health, observes:

> There is little doubt among those who are most active in research in this field that an understanding of the biology of aging is within reach of this generation, providing that a sufficient priority in terms of good brains, sound financing, adequate facilities and administrative support is given this undertaking.

When such information is finally known, the extent to which complete rejuvenation would be possible will depend on two factors: (1) The degree of irreversible brain damage caused by the aging process prior to the start of rejuvenation therapies. (2) The fundamental nature of the aging process itself: Is it a comparatively simple pattern of progressive chemical alternation that can be controlled, or is it an exceedingly complex pattern of biological changes that may be slowed down, but not reversed to any significant extent? We will not know to what degree rejuvenation may be possible until all of the causes of biological aging are completely understood.

In their efforts to arrive at such an understanding, gerontologists have found that the life-spans of other animals provide sources of useful information. The reader may be surprised to find that man is the longest-lived mammal, and one of the longest-lived vertebrates. Alex Comfort points out that the Indian elephant is the mammal with the life-span nearest to man, about 60 to 70 years. Whales usually live 30 to 50 years. The hippopotamus and rhinoceros may live 50 years or more. Other large animals including African elephants, horses, domestic cattle, and lions live 30 to 40 years.

Smaller animals usually have shorter life-spans. The shrew is the smallest mammal with a maximum life-span of two years and an average life-span of less than one year. The life-span of some birds is much longer. The reported average age for eagles is 80, for parrots 75 to 100, and for vultures 100 to 110.

The life-spans of some of the larger fish are not accurately known. Comfort points out that a 720 kg. sturgeon should be about 200 years old, and occasional examples weighing 1,200 to 1,600 kg. would be of fantastic antiquity since growth rate declines with age and size. Unfortunately, fin ray section studies were not made on these huge sturgeon, and they may have been examples of freak gigantism.

According to Alex Comfort, "the longevity of tortoises is one of the few popular beliefs about animals' life-span which is correct, though it has been exaggerated." The tortoise has a life-span of 150 to 200 years and may be the longest-lived animal.

The larger tortoises, in fact, and certain species of fish never stop growing. These animals remain fertile throughout their lives and do not exhibit the physical deterioration that characterizes senescence in mammals. If some of these creatures are really capable of growing indefinitely, then they should not age at all. The hypothesis that warm-blooded vertebrates grow old primarily because they have a fixed adult size will be reexamined throughout this book.

The differences between the aging rates of related species is of great importance to the study of senescence, and is a relatively unexplored area of gerontology. Man lives an average of 70 to 80 years, and our nearest relatives, the chimpanzee, gibbon, and gorilla apparently live only 30 to 40 years. These mammals are in roughly the same size range as man. Smaller primates have still shorter lives. A South American monkey, the pigmy marmoset, is the smallest of the primates and has an average life-span of 8 to 10 years.

The life-spans of lower creatures are interesting phenomena to the student of experimental gerontology. Examples of plant longevity are equally intriguing. For instance, the oldest living things on earth are the bristle cone pines in the White Mountains near the California-Nevada border. Many of these small trees, found at altitudes of 9,000 to 12,000 feet, are more than 4,000 years old. It must be remembered, however, that such studies of primitive organisms and plant life-spans do not include the key to man's achieving comparable longevity. Gerontology research, from the vantage point of the 1960's, does not promise that senility will be eliminated, but it does suggest new possibilities for the extension of active, productive years.

The advantages of a longer life-span are, of course, innumerable. The working years of people in all occupations would be extended, benefiting both themselves and society. The vigor of youth could be combined with the wisdom of a long lifetime of fruitful experience.

One of the great wasted resources today is the talents of our senior citizens. Executives, professors, and skilled technicians are turned out to pasture at 65, regardless of their ability to produce. The entire concept of an arbitrary retirement age should be reconsidered. In the future, mandatory retirement might be based on a scientific measurement of biological aging stemming from advanced knowledge in gerontology.

The productive lives of the unusually brilliant and creative people of society would be extended and progress in all fields thereby accelerated. Many men have made valuable contributions long after any arbitrary retirement age. Edison made important discoveries in his seventies and he started pioneering studies on the production of synthetic rubber when he was 83. At 79 Paderewski was still a master of the piano, giving concerts before large audiences. At 83 Alfred Tennyson published one of his most memorable poems, "Crossing the Bar." At 78 Benjamin Franklin was ambassador to France and at 80 wrote his autobiography. Adenauer was Chancellor of Germany in his late eighties and Churchill was Prime Minister in his early eighties.

An extended "prime of life" would also mean more time for

education. As human knowledge increases, the time spent to acquire a necessary body of useful knowledge also increases. Today few individuals have acquired an adequate education until they are 25 or 30. In the future this education might require many more years. One solution might be to raise the intelligence of our population (see Chapter 4). But the most obvious answer is to extend the productive years of youthful vitality.

The new progress in gerontology, aided by the experiments of Carrel, Lansing, and McCay, has caused many leading scientists to take an increasingly optimistic view of our chance for victory over the aging process. It is generally thought that the human life-span can be extended to 100 or 150 years. Some scientists believe that breakthroughs are possible that might vastly extend the life-span—perhaps hundreds of years, a millennium or more.

The British Nobel Laureate Sir George Thomson believes that gerontology and geriatrics will eventually lead to "permanent youth," and he foresees its advantages and disadvantages: [4]

> There does not seem to be anything in the nature of the reproduction of tissue which demands its death. . . . I believe medical research should spend increasing effort on the prevention, which at first will be postponement, of old age. It means learning a lot more about physiological processes, especially the more recondite ones. . . . Permanent youth will certainly bring its problems, and the politicians and the preachers of the future may well curse the physiologists as heartily as they do now the inventors of the atomic bombs. Perhaps, however, indeed probably, the process of discovery will be gradual. One cause of senility after another will be found and removed, each resulting in only a minor extension of active life. One cannot help wondering what will happen if the causes are all known and found curable, there would then be no natural term of life. All death would be by accident or intent, for in a sense death by a disease which is well understood and not normally fatal is an accident as much as death in a motor crash.

One can now legitimately speculate on the possibility that gerontology is at the same stage of understanding as was nuclear physics in the mid 1930's. Shortly before his death in 1937, Lord Ernest Rutherford discounted all possibilities that man would ever be able to harness nuclear energy as a practical power source. The Hahn-Strassmann-Meitner experiments in December 1938 presented an unexpected avenue which made all of our present nuclear technology possible. (Note: The announcement of a particularly important physical or biological discovery is called the Hahn-Strassmann point.)

Dr. Otto Hahn received the Nobel Prize in chemistry for identifying the light element barium after bombarding uranium with low-energy neutrons. After analyzing Hahn's discovery, Dr. Lise Meitner and her nephew Dr. Otto R. Frisch deduced the details of the physical mechanism of uranium fission. Analogously, in recent years, we have begun to understand fundamental life processes. DNA and RNA codes and relationships are being discovered and analyzed. One by one, we are beginning to unravel the exact structure of hormones, enzymes, and the other vital chemicals of living organisms. In time all these will be fully understood, and this new knowledge will bring science even closer to the answers in its study of the basic biological causes of aging.

The biological discoveries leading to the Fountain of Youth may be as near to us as practical nuclear energy was when Lord Rutherford made his pessimistic prophecy. Once the important Hahn-Strassmann points in aging are understood and fully accepted by the scientific community, senescence may be slowed down indefinitely. Since its onset is so imperceptible, aging may well be only a series of biochemical changes which, once clarified, may be completely controllable. If this is true, and research into aging is accelerated, the long-sought elixir of life may be within man's immediate reach.

2

~~~~~~~~~~~~~~~~~~~~~~~~~~~~~~~~

Nutrition and Aging

SURVIVING records of ancient civilizations provide the earliest evidence for the still-prevalent belief that a special selection of foods can postpone aging and even effect a degree of rejuvenation. Though we know today that "fad" diets are of questionable value, the relationship between the aging process and nutritional patterns is significant and complex.

The ancients relied on sexual capacity as the most effective means of measuring the revitalizing effects of special diets. All ancient rejuvenation therapies, therefore, have a strong sexual orientation, promising to prevent barrenness in women and the decline in male sexual potency, both of which are the usual accompaniments to senility. These ancient rejuvenation menus are entertaining reading material today. The "blood of young virgins" (preferably beautiful virgins) is frequently a key ingredient to the diet, and a variation of this theme includes avoiding the flesh of older animals. Special roots, eggs, snail heads, and herbs are suggested in an almost unending variety. While some of these rejuvenation menus appear ludicrous today, others are surprisingly in accord with current standards of proper nutrition.

The belief that certain foods rejuvenate and extend life is

33

still very much alive. During the 1950's, the "royal jelly" fad with its promises of renewed youth had all the characteristics of the ancient aphrodisiac menus. Royal jelly is the substance produced in the bodies of worker bees and is the sole source of nutrition for queen bees. Queen bees grow much larger than worker bees, lay their own weight in eggs each day for years, and live 10 to 15 times longer than the worker bees. If royal jelly had such an extraordinary effect on the queen bee, increasing fertility and longevity, it should prove equally rejuvenating for people—so reasoned the faddists. Royal jelly was made available in expensive foods, and compounded in women's face creams. But the fad faded because it demonstrated no more rejuvenation effects than the blood of young virgins.

In addition to nutritive value, some of the ancient dietary rejuvenation proposals have a considerable degree of scientific validity. Indeed, McCay's dietary experiments owe much to early longevity analysis. In the late fifteenth century Francis Bacon wrote: [1]

> It seems to be approved by experience that a sparse diet, and almost a pythagorical, such as is either prescribed by the strict rules of a monastic life, or practiced by hermits which have necessity and poverty for their rule, rendereth a man long lived.

Luigi Cornaro, Venetian nobleman and a contemporary of Francis Bacon, achieved historic longevity through a sparse diet. Cornaro was born in Venice in 1464 and led an active and varied life until he died in Padua in 1566. As a young man, Cornaro suffered from stomach trouble, and fasting was recommended as a cure. He settled upon a lifetime diet of 12 ounces of solid food (principally eggs) per day, supplemented by 14 ounces of wine. Cornaro was notably productive throughout his long lifetime. He wrote on many subjects, was active in civic affairs, and constructed four villas. At 83, he outlined his dietary formula for long life in a little book, *La Vita Sobria,* which he rewrote when he was 95. Since that time, Cornaro's essay has been widely read and has provided the stimulus for many successful dietary experiments of significant value to gerontologists.

McCay's Dietary Breakthrough

In 1927, the late Dr. Clive M. McCay began the now classic dietary experiments that lengthened the life-span of rats by controlling their intake of food and growth rate. The results of these experiments were first published in 1932. The slow rate of progress in experimental gerontology is underscored by the fact that no one has yet demonstrated a better means of extending mammalian youth and total length of life.

McCay originally wanted to test the hypothesis that mammalian senility is related to initial rapid growth followed by cessation of growth. It had long been observed that the aging process is significantly slower in vertebrates that continue to grow throughout their entire life-span. McCay used dietary underfeeding as a means of producing a long delay in mammalian growth.

McCay's control group rats were given essential protein, minerals and vitamins along with an unlimited supply of calories from a mixture of sugar and lard. They lived a normal life-span, the oldest surviving 969 days. Rats in the underfed group were given the same diet of protein, minerals and vitamins as the controls, but with insufficient calories to maintain normal development. Their growth rate was reduced to a fraction of normal. The underfed rats were maintained in a juvenile state for periods up to 1,000 days. At this point, the caloric intake was increased to reestablish normal growth, and the rats rapidly grew to normal size. The life-span of these retarded rats was almost doubled, the oldest one surviving 1,465 days.

The underfed 1,000-day-old rats had most of the characteristics of young rats in appearance, levels of intelligence, and rate of activity. Their glossy coats were especially characteristic of youth. There were some adverse changes including loss of calcium in the bones (similar to human osteoporosis), and calcification in the aorta and kidneys.

The growth of the rats was not stopped completely because they died if some increase in weight was not allowed. Nor did underfeeding preserve the youthful state indefinitely. In later dietary retardation experiments, McCay found that if the rats were maintained in a juvenile state for 1,150 days, less than half were capable of resuming normal growth.

McCay's 1,000-day-old retarded rats might be compared to a 90-year-old human with the physical appearance of a teenager. This pioneer work is an important breakthrough because McCay disproved the theory that the life-span is species-limited. Of even greater significance, he proved that the mammalian life-span can be doubled and the period of youth as a percentage of the total life-span increased. Every responsible theory of aging must include an explanation of why McCay's retardation experiments were successful.

McCay's experiment has been repeated several times, including an impressive effort by the Soviet scientist Dr. V. N. Nikitin of the University of Kharkov. Experiments on mice have produced similar results, increasing both their total and reproductive life-spans.

There are many interesting variations of McCay's experiment that would be useful in experimental gerontology. Dr. Robert S. de Ropp has speculated on the possibility of conducting rat growth retardation experiments in germ-free chambers, thereby eliminating the lung diseases which usually kill the older rats. One recent experiment employed a synthetic diet in which the amino acid trytophan was withheld from mice, thereby halting the maturing process for 9 months. When the chemical was restored they started growing again, and lived twice their normal life-span.

Moderate Dietary Restriction

Experiments have been conducted on rats in which food intake was reduced only moderately, to a level that did not inhibit growth or sexual maturation. The results showed a 25 percent increase in the life-span of female rats and a 30 percent increase in the life-span of male rats. Such experiments suggest that some form of dietary restriction might be an effective means of extending life-span. Since normal dieting is not very effective, completely new approaches to weight reduction for humans will be necessary to increase life-span through dietary restriction.

A significant advance in effective weight control was made by Dr. A. P. Simeons, a British physician working in Rome, Italy. Dr. Simeons maintains that the human body has three kinds of fat. The first is the structural fat that supports the body's organs and protects the arteries. The second type of fat, evenly distributed throughout the body, is the normal fuel reserve used by the body when nutritional intake is not sufficient to meet immediate metabolic demands. There is a third type of "abnormal" fat that is not readily available to the body when food intake is reduced. It tends to form in local deposits, creating unattractive bulges.

According to Dr. Simeons, when an obese person goes on a low-calorie diet, he will first lose his normal fat reserves, the most ready source of energy. Only when these are depleted will the abnormal fat reserves be broken down. Consequently, people on low caloric diets are weak, hungry, and tired. Since abnormal fat reserves are the last to be broken down, there is not sufficient redistribution of the unattractive bulges.

Dr. Simeons discovered that daily injections of "human chorionic gonadotrophin" (HCG) caused the abnormal fat to be the first form of body fat broken down, provided the shots were accompanied by a strict diet of only 500 calories a day. HCG is only found in the human body during pregnancy when the placenta produces it in enormous quantities. Its function then is to break down the abnormal fat deposits, thereby insuring the rapidly growing fetus of adequate nutrition regardless of its mother's eating habits. Most of this HCG is eventually excreted in the urine where it can be extracted for injection.

Theoretically, one-half cc. of HCG liberates about 2,000 calories of abnormal fat a day, providing a total of 2,500 readily metabolized calories when added to the 500-calorie diet. Therefore a person under HCG dietary treatment can conduct normal daily activities without any sign of hunger or fatigue.

The first three days of a diet including HCG injections are enjoyable because the patient must gorge himself. This rapid intake of excess food is necessary to replenish the body's normal fat reserves depleted by daily activity. The body is thereby able to adjust to the 500-calorie-a-day diet which follows. Moreover, it takes about three daily injections before abnormally deposited fat begins to circulate and is available to supply the 2,000 additional daily calories which prevent hunger and fatigue. The daily HCG injections are easily administered at home with disposable, sterile hypodermic syringes.

The HCG diet places no restriction on intake of salts, coffee, tea, or mineral water. Vitamin supplements can be taken daily. When HCG breaks up abnormal fatty tissue, only the fat is burned. The protein, vitamins and minerals also blocked in these tissues are returned to the body.

The HCG diet results in weight loss of close to a pound a day. Patients who need to lose 15 pounds or less require a 26-day treatment with 23 daily injections. The extra three injections are necessary because the patient must continue the 500-calorie diet three days after the last injection. If he starts eating normally while there is even a trace of HCG in his body, he puts on weight at an alarming rate. Forty days is the maximum for the HCG diet. After that time, patients begin to show signs of HCG immunity. The diet can be resumed after six weeks when the immunity wears off. If a patient has only five pounds of abnormal fat to lose, he will become ravenously hungry in spite of continued injections. This is the sign that all abnormal fat is gone, and these patients must then be put on a 800–1,000-calories-a-day diet for the remainder of the 26 days.

Dr. Simeons suggests that HCG acts on the hypothalamus, that part of the brain which regulates all the endocrine glands as well as the metabolizing of fat and sugar. Since the hypothalamus seems to be involved in many disorders associated with obesity, Dr. Simeons believes that the treatment for obesity requires a decrease in strain on the hypothalamus so that the gland can function normally. For that reason too, the HCG treatment should never be given for less than 26 days (23 daily injections and three more days while the HCG is still in the system).

There are other research findings that help to explain HCG's role in weight reduction. Growth hormone, a vital body chemical produced in the pituitary gland and which regulates growth, is thought to play an important role in freeing fatty acids from abnormal fat deposits. These released acids change the deposit fat from a "hardened" form into an unsaturated form which can enter the blood plasma and be used as a fuel for metabolic processes. The role of HCG may be that it causes the hypothalamus to secrete chemical messengers which stimulate the pituitary gland into increased growth hormone production. Other fat-mobilizing hormones produced by the pituitary gland in addition to growth hormone have recently been discovered. More will be said about HCG and growth hormone in Chapter 4.

HCG also acts on cholesterol and therefore may help prevent arteriosclerosis. Blood plasma cholesterol circulates in two forms, "free" or unsaturated and "esterified" or hardened.

Normally these fats are present in a proportion of about 25 percent free to 75 percent esterified cholesterol, the esterified cholesterol being the agent which damages artery walls. In pregnancy the proportion is reversed. For this reason arteriosclerosis never gets worse during pregnancy. During the treatment of obesity with the HCG diet, the portion of free to esterified cholesterol undergoes the same reversal. However, if the total amount of circulating cholesterol is normal before treatment, this absolute amount neither increases nor decreases significantly.

When an obese patient with abnormally high cholesterol blood levels, and already showing signs of arteriosclerosis, is treated with HCG, his blood pressure drops, his coronary circulation seems to improve, but his total blood cholesterol soars. At first this increase in cholesterol greatly alarmed Dr. Simeons. However, he observed that the patients came to no harm even if treatment was continued. In follow-up examinations, some months after the HCG treatment, the cholesterol blood levels were much lower than before treatment. Dr. Simeons now believes that the rise in cholesterol levels is entirely due to the liberation of recent cholesterol deposits that have not yet undergone calcification in the arterial wall.

One alternative to HCG treatment is a somewhat drastic operation that has been performed on grossly overweight patients. The body absorbs most of its fat through the wall of the lower small bowel. By shortening that absorbing wall, surgeons have limited the assimilation of fat. Perhaps a modified version of this operation might be applicable to patients with less severe weight control problems.

The effects of small bowel shortening can be duplicated chemically. Dr. Robert L. Fuson of Duke University has discovered that a resin called cholestyramine binds itself to bile acids in the digestive tract so that they are expelled in the feces. This reaction causes the liver to replace these bile acids using cholesterol already in the body as a raw material. Con-

sequently, there is a sharp drop in cholesterol levels. Cholestyramine also reduces the absorption of other fats into the
blood. Patients taking cholestyramine three times a day before
each meal have lost all excess weight and maintained slender
figures without dieting.

Cholestyramine may be the long-sought answer to the problem of cholesterol and obesity. It would painlessly provide the
life-extending benefits of a sparce diet in addition to reducing
the incidence of atherosclerosis.

Gerontological Nutritional Research Needed

To effectively extend the lives of adults 10 percent or more
by nutritional modification will require a much better understanding of the components of an ideal human diet than we
now have. Rat experiments can provide guidelines in determining the caloric intake that will promote longevity, but
extensive tests on humans are necessary in order to establish
the optimum mixture of vitamins, minerals and other essential
nutrients.

Changing the composition of our diets is not likely to result
in any significant extension of the life-span. People who are
in good health in the 90 to 100 age range do not show any
consistency in the foods they eat, although they tend to be
thin. Many who reach an advanced age are not temperate in
food and drink or tobacco. The extent to which dietary modification can prolong youth will depend on the fundamental
nature of the aging process itself, not on some unique combination of foods.

Even so, health food stores promote ocean salt, garlic pills,
apple cider vinegar, and a bewildering variety of "natural"
food as panaceas for the ills of mankind. Several recent books
have applied this nutritional nonsense to the aging field by
proposing that senescence is primarily caused by improper
diet. Most of these books recommend organically grown food
and blame all of our troubles on the use of chemical fertilizers.

There is nothing wrong with organically grown food, but it effects no rejuvenation miracles. Animal experiments have demonstrated that rats fed on organically grown food have the same average life-span as rats fed on completely synthetic food, as long as the caloric intake is the same.

The fact, however, that the public is confused and uncertain about proper diet reinforces the vital need for greatly expanded research in an effort to answer the nutritional unknowns. While the significance to gerontology of the results may not be dramatic, the clarification of the relationship of certain trace elements, fatty acids, and other nutrients to cardiovascular diseases, obesity, diabetes, and arthritis will help control disease.

Clearly, there is no single "miracle" substance that will reverse or even inhibit the aging process. There is, however, a great deal of knowledge already available about dietary requirements and about elements within the body that can be controlled to improve health and thereby postpone some of the effects of aging. Most important among these nutritional tools are vitamin therapy, the regulation of trace elements, and synthetic foods.

Vitamin Therapy

Vitamins are organic compounds necessary for normal growth and health. The thousands of different enzymes in the body are essentially protein and vitamin complexes. Enzymes play a catalytic role in the transformation of energy and in the regulation of all metabolic functions.

Vitamins will be important therapeutic agents in our anti-aging elixir when more is known about their exact role in human metabolism. It is the "pharmacodynamic" action of vitamins—their use as drugs—that is of interest to experimental gerontology. This application involves huge doses of specific vitamins. Though excessive quantities of some vitamins, notably vitamin D, can be toxic, massive doses of other vitamins actually help to counter certain biochemical processes that contribute to biological senescence.

Vitamin E is of particular interest as an anti-aging drug. Vitamin E is actually a complex of several similar compounds, the most effective being alpha tocopherol. It is essential for reproduction in rats and probably in humans. Vitamin E is also an effective antioxidant. It reduces oxygen requirements in the tissues by regulating the oxidation of fats and the utilization of carbohydrates and protein in the body. Vitamin E dilates capillaries and rapidly increases collateral circulation when an area is deprived of normal blood supply. It prevents the overproduction of scar tissue and plays a role in preserving the strength of capillary walls. These properties make vitamin E particularly useful as a preventative agent in the fight against arteriosclerosis, the disease that almost invariably accompanies senescence.

The application of vitamin E to combat cardiovascular disease was pioneered by the Canadian physicians W. E. and E. V. Shute. They found it useful in the treatment of all diseases characterized by decreases in local oxygen supply. Their findings were confirmed by Soviet scientists who used a mixture of vitamins E and A (there is a close association between these two vitamins in the body). The Russian investigators reported that their vitamin E and A supplements given to older patients caused "a surge of strength, disappearance of overall weakness, improvement of sleep, and disappearance of headaches along with such aging characteristics as face wrinkles. Patients were able to walk 2 to 5 times as far after treatment as before and in some the hair turned black." The Russian scientists attributed these benefits to "properties that strengthen the ability of the tissues to absorb oxygen, restore impaired circulation in the tiniest blood vessels, and substantially help to restore the normal permeability of the vascular endothelium."

The exaggerated therapeutic claims of vitamin E enthusiasts, coupled with articles in the lay press suggesting that it can turn docile men into conquering Casanovas, undoubtedly has hindered research into the real role it may play in aging. It sounds too much like the elixir sought by the discredited alchemists. The effectiveness of vitamin E should not, however, be underestimated, for it may well live up to even the most dramatic expectations.

In addition to preventing arteriosclerosis, vitamin E may directly modify the aging process by acting upon a yellowish-black inert substance called lipofuscin that accumulates in the long-lived or fixed cells of the body (brain, heart, etc.). Lipofuscin is a mixture of a fluorescent chemical and a fatty or lipidal material that seems to be produced by oxidation. It occupies 10 percent of the volume of old cells, and in some cases 30 percent or more. The antioxidant action of vitamin E may slow down the rate of lipofuscin production within the cells. Other vitamins may also play a part, as yet undiscovered, in the modification of senescence.

When taken together in specific ratios, vitamins exhibit interesting synergistic properties. Some vitamin combinations produce adverse reactions on the body; massive doses of certain vitamins can result in symptoms of deficiencies of other vitamins. Therefore, successful vitamin research is not simply determining the effects on the body of large quantities of each vitamin, but the effects of increased quantities of two or more vitamins in different ratios. The end result may be a delicate balance of vitamin ratios that will vary for each person undergoing therapy.

In addition to the discovery of natural vitamins, biochemists have produced new substances by modifying the molecular structure of the current vitamin family. Some of these compounds emerging from the new "genesis" of biochemistry will play an important role in general nutrition and in the prevention of senescence.

Trace Elements

Trace elements, the quantitatively minute chemicals present at all times in the human body, show a gradual, sometimes dramatic increase throughout all tissues as the body ages. Though this increase is thought to contribute to biological senescence, the proper intake and excretion of specific trace elements are essential to good nutrition and help prevent certain diseases.

Trace elements presently known to be necessary for normal body function are: calcium, phosphorus, sodium, potassium, chlorine, magnesium, iron, copper, iodine, fluorine, zinc, molybdenum, manganese and vanadium. Minute amounts of certain trace elements are essential components of key enzymes. Vanadium is of especial interest to gerontologists because it appears to inhibit the formation of cholesterol, reduces the incidence of gallstones and may therefore be part of an enzyme that helps prevent arteriosclerosis. A threefold increase in magnesium intake also appears to lower blood cholesterol levels and the incidence of kidney damage. A proper intake of zinc assures healthy bone and protein repair.

Potassium is thought to play a vital role in the control of heart disease. Some scientists believe that the proper functioning of heart cells depends on maintaining a proper balance between intracellular potassium levels and sodium levels outside the cells. Massive injections of potassium (in solution with glucose and insulin) have been administered with great effectiveness in a wide variety of serious heart disorders. Perhaps a better nutritional balance between potassium and sodium intake could significantly reduce the incidence of heart disease.

Recent investigations disclose that fluoride helps prevent two of the diseases which most often accompany old age: osteoporosis, a bone-softening disease common in older women, and hardening of the arteries. It was reported that in a low-fluoride water area, osteoporosis in women was seven times greater than in the high-flouride area, and twice as many older men had aorta calcium deposits. If additional investigations confirm these findings, and evidence of reduced calcification is found in other vascular tissues, especially the brain arteries, fluoride will assume an important role in preventing cardiovascular disease and osteoporosis. Since too high a fluoride content in the water damages children's teeth, the fluoride would have to be taken in pill form.

Excessive quantities of certain trace elements can cause serious disease. For example, while minute amounts of copper are necessary for normal cell function, too much copper will cause damage by acting as a catalyst in excessively rapid oxidation of fats in the blood. Dr. Denham Harman, of the University of Nebraska College of Medicine, believes that the by-products of this oxidation act as irritants on blood vessel walls and promote the formation of fatty deposits. If the foregoing is correct then polyunsaturated fats, because of their ready oxidation, may produce more harmful effects on arteries than diets high in saturated fats.

Dr. Harman has compared the copper levels of 30 men age 35 to 55, each with a history of at least one heart attack, against those of 95 others with no heart disease. He found that the heart attack group's blood copper level was significantly higher. These data suggest that a lowering of serum copper levels—by dietary or chemical means—and/or increased dietary intake of antioxidants, such as vitamin E, would tend to decrease the chance of developing clinical atherosclerosis (heart attack, stroke, etc.). Moreover, the present trend of raising dietary levels of polyunsaturated fats may, on a long-term basis, actually increase the incidence of clinical atherosclerosis even though polyunsaturated fats lower serum cholesterol levels.

Dr. Henry A. Schroeder, a Dartmouth Medical School physiologist, has recently reported that cadmium may be the principal cause of high blood pressure (hypertension). He observed that hypertensive patients excreted abnormally large amounts of cadmium in their urine. Other investigators found that persons who had died of hypertension had abnormally high cadmium levels in their kidneys. Kidney function is important in regulating blood pressure and many cases of hypertension are clearly associated with kidney disorders.

Dr. Schroeder constructed a special animal experimentation facility to confirm the relationship between cadmium and hypertension. The laboratory was constructed of wood to insure that the animals were not accidentally exposed to trace metals. Pure air was piped into the facility from a nearby forest and was filtered to remove all dust particles. The water supply from a natural spring was double-filtered. Laboratory investigators even removed their shoes before entering the laboratory. Cadmium-free rats in this environment showed no signs of high blood pressure, while rats given minute traces of cadmium salts developed a disease with most of the characteristics of human hypertension.

A chemical called CDTA-zinc binds itself to cadmium in the body so that the cadmium is excreted more readily. Dr. Schroeder found that the blood pressure of hypertensive rats given CDTA-zinc dropped to normal within a week. Such results encourage a more extensive search for other chemicals that, by binding themselves to harmful trace elements, facilitate more effective excretion.

In the course of his cadmium research, Dr. Schroeder discovered that chromium deficiency in rats produced diabetes accompanied by artery damage similar to progressive human diabetes. Rats maintained at a normal chromium level had no diabetes or arteriosclerosis. It is possible that continued research on the effects of specific trace elements will reveal that most of the degenerative diseases associated with aging are actually caused by trace element deficiencies or toxic excesses.

Administering therapeutic quantities of beneficial trace elements is simple. Avoiding compounds containing harmful mixtures or trace elements is much more difficult. For instance, there is an excess of cadmium in coffee, tea, refined flour, polished rice, and oysters. Cadmium is introduced into our drinking water because it is a contaminate of copper used in galvanized pipes. In some areas, it is a component in air pollution.

Atmospheric pollution is the fastest-growing source of trace element poisoning. The tetraethyl lead in gasoline is rapidly being transferred to humans via smog. In many areas with severe air pollution, lead blood levels are 100 times greater than normal. Polonium-210, a radioactive element, is mixed with the lead in "antiknock" compounds and is present in smog. There is no question that technological solutions to the smog problem are vital to future health.

The harmful effects of smoking are attributable, in part, to the presence of specific trace elements. Lead arsenate is widely used in tobacco insecticides. Moreover, the tobacco plant acts as a biological concentrator of polonium-210, which emits alpha particles that can be particularly active in initiating harmful changes in protein structure. Extremely high concentrations of polonium-210 are found in the lung tissues of lung cancer victims. If polonium-210 is proven to be the principal cause of diseases associated with heavy smoking, then a relatively "safe" form of polonium-free tobacco might be grown through hydroponic techniques. National prohibition demonstrated that it is almost impossible to separate man from his pleasurable vices. Therefore, science must attempt to make the vices less damaging rather than publish an endless catalog of the dire consequences of their continuation.

Dr. Albert Tyler of the California Institute of Technology has found that the removal of harmful trace elements with metal-chelating agents (chemicals which can selectively bind themselves to specific elements, permitting them to be removed from the body) increases the life of sperm cells several hundred percent in such widely different species as sea urchins and cattle. Dr. Tyler's discovery points the way to precise trace element control throughout our lives, with important aging-deceleration implications.

Synthetic Food

Chemists have synthesized all of the known vitamins, all 22 amino acids that make up plant and animal protein, all essential fatty acids, and the simpler carbohydrates including glucose, levulose, lactose, and sucrose. Several years ago a completely synthetic liquid diet for animals was perfected at the National Cancer Institute. The diet consists of the essential and nonessential L-amino acids, glucose as a source of carbohydrates, and the essential fatty acids, vitamins and trace elements. By omitting any single component of the diet, it is possible to discover the role each nutrient substance plays in animal cancers and also to explore the other relationships between nutrition and senescence. Synthetic diets will enable gerontologists to explore completely every relationship between nutrition and aging.

The natural foods we eat contain many substances noxious to the human body if consumed in sufficient quantities. We consume only moderate amounts of these toxic components, but no one knows what their long-term effects on aging may be. Science has already advanced to the point where it is now possible to produce synthetic foods free of harmful substances. These synthetics can eventually be superior to natural foods in nutritive value, taste and texture.

Synthetic diets should also enable scientists to resolve the nutritional debate over the relationship of fat, particularly cholesterol, to arteriosclerosis. The three fatty acids essential to normal body function are linoletic, arachidonic, and linolenic acid. The body burns fat at a slower rate than it does carbohydrates. Certain fats are better than others as fuel for the body. The fat content of synthetic foods could be restricted to the three essential fatty acids. Such diets will also help determine what the optimum quantities of these fatty acids are, and this information can in turn be applied to the fat content of synthetic foods.

All food proteins are ultimately broken down into amino acids. The body requires the essential amino acids in a definite proportion that differs from the proportion of these amino acids in the undigested protein of foods. If one essential amino acid is deficient, it limits the utilization of the others. Synthetic diets can be composed of amino acids, vitamins, minerals, fatty acids, and carbohydrates in the optimum combinations not available in natural foods.

It is especially important to correct the common belief that synthetic foods must be only in the form of flavored liquids or pills. Since synthetic foods can have any taste or form we desire, gourmets and epicures have nothing to fear.

Further progress in colloidal chemistry and in the study of macromolecules should make it possible to produce synthetic nutrients, jells and filaments of any desired consistency and texture. Polymer science has uncovered the general principles for making substances with different structures and molecular weights so as to be syrupy, gell-like, elastic, tough, brittle, or fibrous.

Research into the chemicals that produce taste sensations should make it possible to identify, synthesize and combine all of the major constitutents, making possible an exact duplication of natural flavor. Perhaps science can even improve on natural flavors and create the "nectar" and "ambrosia" consumed by the gods of Greek mythology.

Synthetic foods which duplicate the form and flavor of natural foods will probably be more expensive, even when mass-produced. But the benefits of the optimum mixture of nutrients they provide would justify the higher costs. Alcoholic beverages could also be synthetically produced that eliminate the minute quantities of fusel oil and acetaldehyde that help cause hangovers.

Anti-Aging Food Patterns

A precisely controlled nutritional intake, which synthetic foods will make possible, is likely to be an important part of any effective anti-aging therapy. Variety, spice, and culinary adventure will still remain. The degenerative diseases that accompany aging could be partly controlled, though not eliminated, by improved nutritional intake and by effective excretion of toxic substances.

Future anti-aging programs should encourage people to eat less. Perhaps HCG weight reduction sessions, two or three times a year, will become standard. Vitamin E and other vitamins could be administered in massive doses. New trace elements will be added to the diet and increasingly sophisticated chemical methods will rid the body of damaging compounds. None of these additions are incompatable with the most exotic dishes prepared by skilled chefs or with grandmother's favorite recipe. An infinite variety of synthetic foods served side by side with traditional dishes would combine to make the added years of extended youth healthy and satisfying.

3

〜〜〜〜〜〜〜〜〜〜〜〜〜〜〜〜〜〜〜〜

Environment, Exercise, Relaxation, and Sleep

UTOPIAS and Shangri-Las have never, alas, existed beyond the realm of fiction. An ideal environment, unspoiled by high population density and the toxic by-products of a complex industrial society, has never been achieved. We are not certain, therefore, what the average life-span lived under ideal conditions would be.

Most of us are children of a technological civilization and spend the greater part of our lives in crowded urban areas. The environment parameters in our major cities have a deteriorating influence on human longevity. Our fundamental goal of extending youth must, therefore, encompass city planning, transportation systems, communications and all other crucial elements in the man-machine interface. Urban man must refine alternate life-extending corrections by the wise use of science and technological innovation, coupled with the intelligent apportioning of his own physical and psychological resources.

Exercise and Relaxation

Many exercise and dietary enthusiasts are part of a larger "back to nature" movement. A bizarre example of this cult is the promise of a "100-year life-span" through exercise running around nudist camps and including a vegetarian diet of raw fruit and vegetables (organically grown). Such a pattern is no more likely to greatly extend life than a comparable amount of exercise in a hotel room combined with a diet of champagne, caviar and raw oysters. Exercise is, however, extremely important in extending youthful vitality though there is no scientific evidence to prove that it significantly extends total life-span. Dr. Laurence Morehouse of UCLA has achieved impressive results in a program of regular exercise for subjects ranging in age from 30 to 80 years. After a prescribed exercise regimen their physical stamina and mental agility were noticeably improved. Some of his subjects, for example, were professors in their thirties and forties who had gone into a period of professional and physical decline. As a result of the exercise program almost all of them increased their output of scholarly papers, their teaching improved, and they became sexually more active.

The life-extending benefits of exercise most likely result from a reduction in the incidences of certain degenerative diseases rather than from any direct modification of the aging process itself. Some investigators claim, for example, that regular exercise reduces the incidence of arteriosclerosis. If proper exercise could reduce the incidence of arteriosclerosis by 50 percent, it would add three or four years to the average life-span.

There is a diversity of exercise patterns among people who live to advanced ages, though many specialists report that swimming and walking are among the best forms of exercise for elderly people.

For the urban commuter, however, with all modes of transportation immediately available, the amount of regular walking he does is minimal. Most people would rather ride than walk. Moreover, as the cities become more crowded, many commuters are forced to spend more time in transit, time which could otherwise have been spent in exercise and recreation. Foreseeable increases of both people and cars means that our highways will increasingly tend to become "parking lots" during the rush hours. In the evening many automobile commuters require a therapeutic double scotch or martini to unwind from the strain of erratic rush-hour traffic.

We cannot change the fundamental characteristics of a complex industrial society. Better city planning, perhaps incorporating novel transportation systems, will be some help. An approach favored by Soviet planners, locating the residence closer to the workplace is worthy of consideration. But primarily, each individual must carefully evaluate his own habits and alter them so that exercise and relaxation are included in proper balance.

Further Environmental Considerations

Other negative environmental factors are outside the immediate control of single individuals. Atmospheric pollution is unquestionably the fastest-growing health menace. Others are equally harmful. We all inhale some DDT and other pesticides. Pesticides are present in our food. Their effect on the aging process? Well, they certainly don't extend insect life and can produce sterility in birds and other vertebrates. We are also subject to a certain amount of background radiation which probably shortens life. There is evidence that increased city noise is becoming a serious health problem because it increases stress. All these environmental factors affect disease processes and may also have some direct influence on the rate of biological aging.

There are some environmental unknowns that may also influence aging. The earth's magnetic field is one example. There is as yet no evidence about the effects of higher or lower magnetic fields on aging. There are also many trace elements in key body enzymes that might be the mechanism of magnetic field biological variations. Mice are the largest animals to have been exposed to varying magnetic fields, and results have been contradictory. In one test, a mouse exposed to 4,000 Gauss for 4 weeks retained a youthful appearance accompanied by increased alertness. But in another experiment, a group of 7-week-old mice died within 10 days when exposed to a field intensity of 5,000 Gauss. Other experiments using two generations of flies showed no deviation from normal as a result of exposure to a magnetic field, except for faster movement in the 5,000 Gauss field. Magnetic fields may not have any significant effect on the aging process, but biomagnetics could present some surprises of significance to gerontologists.

Gravity is another environmental factor that might influence aging. Arthur C. Clarke believes that man would age more slowly on the moon because of its low gravity.

Life originated in the sea, the evolutionary step that animals took out of the oceans led them to "the alien, hostile element of dry land." There, life came under the crushing influence of gravity, no longer enjoying the "almost zero-g buoyancy" of floating and swimming in the water. . . . A whole legion of bodily troubles—from fallen arches to postural defects, and perhaps even heart strain—have arisen as the direct result of our incessant fight against gravity. . . . It may well be that our potential life span is shortened by this continuous battle against the single g on earth's surface. Men may live longer under 1/6g on the moon than on 1 g earth.

Dr. Jiro Oyama at the NASA Ames Research Center in California recently was able to increase the life-span of two female rats 25 percent over controls by subjecting them to between three and four times normal gravity (a 3 to 4 g environment) on a centrifuge for 47 months. The longevity gain can probably be explained by the depletion of body fat in the increased gravity environment which prevented arteriosclerosis. Dr. Stephen H. Dole of the Rand Corporation cautions that small mammals are far less subject to gravity than large animals the size of man. Consequently the centrifuge experiments are not directly transferable to the extension of human life.

It is doubtful that a human could live in even a 2 g environment for months or years. As mammals increase in size, a lower g environment would seem to promote longevity. The largest animal on earth, the blue whale, will suffocate from its own body weight if it is cast on a beach.

Perhaps in the late 1970's animal experiments on a lunar base will give us the answers to relationships between gravity and aging and clever refinement could control this unique environmental ingredient for our youth-extending elixir.

Sleep

People in the 75-to-95-year age range who show no signs of mental senility seem to have only one thing in common: they sleep well. Older people who develop good exercise habits enjoy better sleep. All the environmental factors mentioned above influence the quality and quantity of sleep.

There is good reason to believe that proper sleep can forestall the aging process. Toxic substances associated with fatigue are likely to have an important relationship to senescence. Dr. Robert S. de Ropp points out that these toxic substances [1]

> are formed each day as a result of the ordinary stresses of waking life and their formation is almost certainly increased by anxiety and mental or emotional strain. Sleep, profound and untroubled, may be regarded as the means whereby these daily accumulations of toxic products are eliminated from the body. Such perfect sleep, however, becomes rarer as the individual ages. The sleep of the aged is notoriously shallow and easily broken. So we may guess that toxins normally removed by sleep are less adequately eliminated as a man grows older, that this, in turn affects the quality of sleep, so that a vicious circle develops, resulting in further accumulation of toxins.

During the 1950's, sleep therapy—long periods of drug-induced sleep—was in vogue in Europe. German sleep clinics, where patients were kept unconscious from three to five days, specialized in the "businessman's disease," which was anything from insomnia to hypertension. French and Russian scientists used a similar form of sleep therapy in the treatment of mental illness. Spectacular claims were made for these treatments. A Russian scientist, Dr. S. Braines, reported that sleep therapy partially rejuvenated senile dogs: [2]

> After a three-month course of drug-induced sleep therapy, we noted the disappearance of certain symptoms of senility. We succeeded in prolonging the life span of a 15-year-old dog (Bolgonese) to 21 years. The motor activity and reaction to the surroundings were restored and preserved. We also noted partial restoration of hair growth. It is important to note the animal showed gradual restoration and preservation of the sex instinct. Histological study of an animal that died by accident demonstrated in one of the testicles an intensive process of spermatogenesis. The experiment performed opened up new possibilities and perspectives in eliminating the symptoms of premature senility in human beings and are indicative of the significance of sleep in the prophylaxis of senility.

Less is heard now about sleep therapy, though it is still used in some European and Soviet clinics. It is doubtful whether it has lived up to early expectations.

Technically, physical rest and the state called sleep are separate physiological functions. Physical rest can be achieved without unconsciousness. Sleep is a function of the cerebral cortex area of the brain. Medical evidence indicates that the cerebral cortex actually requires only 1 or 2 hours of deep sleep per 24 hours, a state in which it is completely isolated from all external and internal stimuli. Much of the time spent "sleeping" is actually devoted to arriving at and emerging from this unconscious state. Consequently, for optimum rest, the time required for pre-deep-sleep and post-deep-sleep should be reduced.

The 1 or 2 hours of deep sleep are necessary also to satisfy psychological needs. One scientist observes that "it permits us to dream and go safely insane for a short time each day." If we all require a daily "insanity quotient," it might be better satisfied when we know more about sleep and sleep-inducing parameters.

Though man spends a considerable portion of his life sleeping or attempting to sleep, investigation reveals that relatively little scientific attention has been given to this vitally important phenomena. The sleep research available confirms that busy, productive people particularly are subject to mild or chronic insomnia. Americans spend approximately 125 million dollars a year on prescriptions for sleeping drugs. Despite extensive pharmaceutical research, no satisfactory sleep-inducing compounds have been found. Bold new approaches to the insomnia problem are needed.

Now let us return to Arthur C. Clarke's proposal that because we evolved from ocean vertebrates, gravity has an adverse effect on the aging process. We cannot transfer the earth's population to the moon, but there may be other ways to obtain the benefits of reduced gravity.

Saline water immersion for protracted periods is the only way to simulate weightlessness in a gravity field. The effects of warm saline water immersion on sleep are particularly significant. Sleeping in a liquid environment induces deeper sleep and reduces the time required to obtain optimum rest.

The body spends much of the time in bed seeking relief from the pressures and stresses created by the constant pull of gravity. The proper saline solution, which makes flotation possible, counteracts the stressful effects of gravity and the counterpressure of supporting surfaces and creates a state resembling weightlessness. Anyone who has floated in a swimming pool or on the ocean surface with some type of aquatic breathing device knows how completely relaxing motionless immersion in water can be. After all, before birth we are surrounded by a body temperature saline solution; water immersion may be nature's answer to perfect rest.

There has been one pioneer effort to exploit the potential of sleep in a warm saline water environment. In 1961 Clark T. Cameron founded a company that developed a 92-inch fiberglass tub called the Aquarest. This system contained a saline water solution which was automatically maintained at body temperature. The salinity was approximately the same as human blood to prevent maceration or withering of the skin, with accompanying energy loss. The Aquarest had a series of water jets on the lower sides of the tub which could provide mild circulation or vigorous hydromassage.

Clark Cameron conducted some preliminary experiments with several Aquarest units which indicated that warm saline water immersion reduced the time required for optimum sleep. He also reported that the depth of rest and sleep was significantly enchanced. The Aquarest Corporation ran out of funds before any large-scale sleep experiments could be conducted. All attempts to obtain government research funds for Aquarest sleep investigation were unsuccessful despite the fact that the organization had a distinguished scientific advisory group available to supervise the experiments. There is a very real need for an extensive research program that would confirm or disprove Cameron's preliminary investigations.

One limitation of the Aquarest was that the subjects floated on their backs with a simple buoyant head support. Space weightlessness simulation experiments indicate that it is better for the subjects to float face downward using a special breathing mask or helmet so that the arms and legs can assume positions more conducive to relaxation.

Saline immersion relaxation systems have other hydrotherapy benefits. The perforations in the contoured bottom can provide a therapeutic "bubble massage" of varying intensity. The unit can have a very low-intensity ultrasonic unit which would cleanse the body. These high-frequency sound waves in water are presently being used to treat patients with muscle and joint afflictions as well as other vascular disorders. The therapeutic value of the saline solution itself is considerable. Healthy skin growth, texture and softness might be improved by adding soluble creams and nutrient chemicals to the saline solution. The mineral content of water in various health spas could easily be duplicated if investigation confirms beneficial properties. There are many possible additives. For instance the Russians have reported skin regeneration in older patients by hydrotherapy with a simple solution of bicarbonate of soda.

There are certain other interesting options that might be explored in technologically bold sleep research investigations. The rare, chemically inert gas xenon has been found to be an almost perfect anesthetic with no aftereffects, even after prolonged use. An 80 percent xenon–20 percent oxygen mixture at normal atmospheric pressure will produce unconsciousness in three to five minutes. The other inert gases produce narcosis at significantly higher pressures. Xenon is, however, extremely expensive and a closed-cycle system, permitting it to be reused with very little gas loss, will be necessary before it can be widely utilized in surgery. There have been no aftereffects reported in the use of xenon narcosis and it is possible, therefore, that people can be safely subjected to it every day. Xenon surgical anesthetic systems can be used very effectively in sleep research experiments.

A somewhat exotic form of relaxation is lung rest by the cessation of breathing. A device called "the equalizing pressure chamber" has been used in experimental lung-rest therapy for tuberculosis patients. This is a system which causes oxygen to enter the lungs and carbon dioxide to be expelled by raising and lowering the cycle of pressures within the unit. The air density within the lungs changes but the volume remains constant, permitting a complete cessation of movement in the muscles used for breathing. The changing pressures are applied equally to all other parts of the body.

Patients describe the nonbreathing state as an extremely pleasant, soothing sensation. Doctors have noted decreased heart action and a beneficial effect on the central nervous system. The impulse to move the limbs diminishes so that patients lie still for hours.

Equalizing pressure chambers could be combined in a system with the other relaxation techniques. The pressure density cycle rate could be automatically controlled by compact devices which measure the amount of carbon dioxide being expelled through the lungs.

The fruition of relaxation-sleep technology will require a significant adjustment on the part of the general public, because it would change an important part of man's daily life, one that has remained constant throughout the history of civilization.

Skeptics may point out the fact that whales, for example, do not have exceptional life spans; but such comparisons are misleading. Whales spend all their lives in cold water that is in constant movement. Their heads are not supported in any way. The sea is full of enemies.

The environment influences aging even before we are born. The manner in which the placenta forms, the mother's diet, disease, drugs she takes and emotions she experiences all have important effects on the development of the fetus. In the years after birth, we gradually are able to make the decisions that allow us to individually select environmental changes. We know that life can be enhanced and extended by an improved environment. Experimental gerontology is making valuable contributions in establishing the guidelines for an advanced urban society which will favor daily habits that tend to strengthen us and help provide the vigor that make the added years a rich experience.

Of equal importance to man's general health and life-span is his internal "environment," created by the hormonal system. A hormone is a chemical substance formed by one organ, that acts as a messenger to regulate and coordinate other organs or tissues in the body. The term came into popular usage around 1914, though it had long been known that "internal secretions" played a vital role in life processes. Hormones are crucial to healthy development of the body and are also being used selectively by scientists for therapeutic purpose. Their role in aging and the prevention of aging is becoming increasingly significant.

4

Hormones, the Elusive Elixir

THE association between sexual function and longevity, established early in human history, continued to influence scientists long after medical research emerged from the superstition and chaos of the Middle Ages. Some extraordinary personalities played well-publicized roles in the early modern attempts to rejuvenate and extend life through the administration of sex hormones. Their colorful story is important in understanding some of the present problems faced by students of gerontology. The use of hormones as a means of extending youth is by no means a closed chapter in experimental gerontology. In fact it is likely to dominate anti-aging therapies for some time to come.

On June 1, 1889, members of the French Société de Biologie assembled to hear an important announcement by Charles Edward Brown-Séquard, professor of physiology at the University of Paris. He enjoyed a prestigious position in French science and occupied the chair formerly held by the great Claude Bernard, father of experimental physiology. Brown-Séquard had developed a reputation for dramatic presentations and spectacular statements. He was a large, swarthy, full-bearded man, skilled in handling an audience. The members of the society that day expected a tantalizing lecture, and they were not disappointed.

Brown-Séquard began by saying: "I have always thought that the weakness of old men was partly due to the diminution of the function of their sexual glands. I am 72 years old. My natural vigor has declined considerably in the last 10 years." He then disclosed that he had prepared a saline solution by grinding up the testicles of young dogs and guinea pigs. After preliminary animal experiments, he began to give himself injections of his solution. Brown-Séquard dramatically concluded: "I have rejuvenated myself by 30 years and today I was able to 'pay a visit' to my young wife."

The average age of the members of the Société de Biologie was 71. One can well imagine their reaction to the practical implications of Brown-Séquard's announcement. The popular press quickly disseminated news of Brown-Séquard's "discovery." There was an immediate market for his serum. He set up a nonprofit organization to prepare large quantities of solution from testicles of bulls.

Brown-Séquard had the right idea, but he used the wrong solvent. His saline solution could not possibly isolate enough testicular hormone to have any effect. His rejuvenation serum was simply salt water, and proved to be a complete failure.

The scientific community denounced Brown-Séquard. His young wife deserted him and he retreated to Menton, France, where he soon died of a cerebral hemorrhage. The tragedy of these events lies in the fact that he was so close to making a far-reaching discovery. The outline of modern endocrinology can be found in the notes he prepared toward the end of his life. His story should be heeded by present-day critics of the gerontologists who offer bold theories which may only require "the correct solvent" for experimental verification. Let the skeptics beware, for scientific achievements tend to far exceed the most optimistic predictions of learned scientists.

The next scientist to attempt rejuvenation through sexual

revitalization was an Austrian medical doctor, Eugen Steinach, professor of physiology at the University of Vienna. He was another commanding figure with a full beard and the outward bearing of an Austrian grand duke. In 1890 Steinach started a series of experiments which he summarized 30 years later in a book entitled *Rejuvenation Through the Experimental Revitalization of the Aging Puberty Gland.* For many years Steinach's publications in scientific journals were only read by other research specialists. But the use of the word "rejuvenation" in his 1920 book was to bring both fame and controversy.

Steinach reasoned that he could stimulate the hormone-producing part of the testicles by destroying the sperm-producing part. He accomplished this through sterilization, tying off and severing the tube (vas deferens) through which the sperm is carried to its storage place in the seminal vesicles. Steinach claimed that this created pressure which damaged the seminal (sperm-producing) tubules in the testicles, causing them to degenerate. Hormone-producing cells would then replace the tubules, thereby increasing the secretion of testosterone from the glands.

Steinach made spectacular claims for his technique and the "Steinach rejuvenation operation" became a surgical fad. The early enthusiasm lasted only until the 1930's, when the mounting weight of medical evidence demonstrated that this operation conferred no rejuvenating benefits. Steinach did not suffer the total defeat of Brown-Séquard because he was eclipsed by a far more controversial scientist who was to be the center of rejuvenation publicity and controversy for many years.

Dr. Serge Voronoff (1866-1951) was a Russian aristocrat who unquestionably ranks as the most formidable figure in the dramatic search for a hormonal Fountain of Youth. He was a handsome man whose charismatic personality completely captivated his audience. Voronoff was multilingual and had the aristocratic bearing of the ruling class of Czarist Russia. It is fitting that Voronoff's rejuvenation theories should emerge from the rather exotic location of an Islamic harem. At the turn of the century, Voronoff was the royal surgeon in the court of the Khedive (King) of Egypt. The ruler maintained a large harem guarded by castrated men known as eunuchs. Voronoff found that the treatment of the court eunuchs demanded a disproportionate amount of his time because these half-men seemed to age quickly and were prone very early to the degenerative diseases characteristic of senescence. He concluded that the source of rejuvenation, perhaps even the secret of life, was to be found in the sexual glands.

Voronoff returned to Europe and perfected his surgical techniques by transplanting animal glands. He removed the testicles from young adult animals, cut them into several narrow segments and attached these testicular segments to the blood-rich membrane of the testicles of an old animal. The membrane was first scraped to insure good capillary contact with the transplant segments and the scrotum was then closed. In a few days the graft took, and presumably revitalizing testosterone poured into the bloodstream.

Voronoff dramatically announced the results of his transplantation experiments in Paris on October 18, 1919, before the 28th French Surgical Congress. He invited interested parties to see several old rams and a bull he had "rejuvenated." Voronoff's commanding appearance, intuitive sense of public appeal, and promised gift to the world—rejuvenation—brought him international attention.

He was besieged by elderly men eagerly seeking their lost youth. Religious objections and legal barriers made it virtually impossible to obtain testicles from the corpses of young men for transplant purposes. A few living volunteers wanted prohibitively high monetary compensation. Voronoff turned to chimpanzees as a source of transplant glands. Between 1920 and 1927 over 1,000 elderly men received the testicles of young chimpanzees.

Though Voronoff claimed lasting effects, his transplants

offered only the illusion of rejuvenation. Today we know that, with the exception of identical twins, transplants will be rejected by the body's immunologic defense mechanism. Only in the last 10 years have immune suppression drugs permitted successful transplants between unrelated humans. Transplants can, however, establish a connection with the host's circulatory system and function for a short time, resulting in a temporary increase of testosterone.

Voronoff's "monkey gland treatment" was detrimental to all parties. The elderly patients paid princely sums for a few days increased hormone supply. We can safely assume that these operations did not add to the happiness of our chimpanzee population.

The Steinach and Voronoff operations had one factor in common—the placebo effect. The term "placebo" refers to any harmless substance containing no medicine and administered only for its psychological effect. Since both Steinach and Voronoff offered supportive testimonials assuring long-term rejuvenation, the placebo effect was probably responsible for the benefits their patients derived.

Today gerontologists tend to be exceedingly critical of the early pioneers such as Voronoff, and overlook the fact that these unsuccessful operations were among the first steps toward the successful organ transplants of the present day. Moreover, the worldwide publicity that Voronoff attracted all through the 1920's and 1930's stimulated other investigations which culminated in the development of artificial hormones.

Voronoff was extremely engaging and generous in the time he gave to anyone interested in the fight against senescence. He had an encyclopediac knowledge of many subjects. Voronoff was dogmatic, but he retained that vital spark seldom found in gerontologists today—the belief that man's intellect will allow him to circumvent the ravages of the aging process. It is interesting to note that most of his fortune came from a wealthy American wife who had the courtesy of not living long, allowing Voronoff to marry a Rumanian princess 40 years his junior.

Gerontology is desperately in need of the public awareness that men such as Voronoff created. Today's scientists tend to be stereotype organization men completely unsuited to propagandizing the revolutionary message of extended youth and life through research. Gerontology needs new Voronoffs who are not afraid of new, sometimes radical experiments and who have the proselytizing spirit to arouse public interest and support.

Hormone Replacement Therapy

In the 1930's, chemists succeeded in isolating natural testosterone. In 1935 a Yugoslavian chemist living in Zurich, Dr. Vladislav Ruzicka, transformed cholesterol into a synthetic testosterone. Soon, many other compounds were synthesized with properties similar to testosterone. Valid hormone replacement experiments were now possible.

Testosterone injections were found to be of great benefit to patients with a true deficiency of the male hormone. Renewed sexual capability was not the only benefit these injections conferred. Testosterone proved to be a powerful anabolic (tissue-building) agent which increased nitrogen retention and protein synthesis. Patients were noticeably rejuvenated, and showed signs of renewed vigor and increased muscle tone.

The leading exponent of testosterone therapy for older men was Dr. Paul de Kruif, who published his views in his book *Male Hormone*.[1] During the past 22 years, however, comparatively few older men have undergone regular testosterone replacement, largely due to the fear of cancer on the part of both patient and physician. There is, however, no evidence that properly administered testosterone increases the incidence of cancer.

It is unfortunate that large-scale testing has not produced the requisite clinical data to resolve all the uncertainties about the administration of testosterone to older men. This treatment remains one of the most effective means presently available of extending youth.

Female sex hormones were synthesized during the 1930's and 1940's and a few courageous physicians immediately began estrogen-replacement therapy. Early experiments seemed to indicate that the administration of estrogen increased the incidence of cancer in mice, and this initial evidence curtailed estrogen replacement in women for many years.

Unlike the male, the female is subject to a sudden curtailment of estrogen during the menopause. The ovaries atrophy and estrogen production diminishes to infinitesimal amounts. The external manifestations of aging become more apparent. The tissues dry out, muscles weaken and skin sags. Even more serious, osteoporosis, or loss of calcium salts, develops, along with an increased susceptibility to arteriosclerosis when the inner artery wall undergoes fatty degeneration.

Cardiovascular illness rarely afflicts premenopause women, though after menopause, women suffer from it with the same frequency as men. Estrogen's biochemical role in protecting women from atherosclerosis is not yet completely understood. It has been successfully administered in small quantities to men suffering from a first heart attack.

Thus the ovary's role in steroid hormone production, crucial to optimum body functioning and tissue repair, is as important as its reproductive function. Dr. William H. Masters, a leading authority in reproduction biology, observes: [2]

> This reduction in steroid secretory activity by the gonad is the "Achilles' heel" of the entire endocrine system during the involutional phase of life. As the result of the inability of the ovary to respond to usual gonadotrophin stimulation, the pituitary-gonadal axis is completely lost. Subsequently, the remaining members of the endocrine chain become uncoordinated secretory organs whose functional involution results from lack of clinical demand, rather than lack of secretory function reserve.

Dr. Masters points out that this same disruption occurs in men, but at a later age, because testosterone production declines only gradually.

Since the decline in stimulation of estrogen production by the pituitary seems to play an important part in aging, it is believed that estrogen replacement can prevent these effects. Over the past 25 years long-term estrogen replacement in post-menopausal women has proven that it is possible to modify or eliminate all the unpleasant changes, with the exception of sterility, brought about by the menopause.

For example, estrogen replacement can prevent or reverse rapid aging of the female genital system. Deprived of estrogen, the vagina frequently becomes stiff and unyielding. In many cases, the vagina decreases in size and is subject to skin cracks that become infected. These changes often make sexual intercourse impossible. Estrogen replacement restores the youthful vaginal mucosa and supple vaginal walls. The vagina returns to its normal size and the skin cracks disappear. There is no evidence that continuous estrogen replacement causes cancer; in fact, one recent study indicates that the incidence of cancer is actually reduced in women receiving estrogen.

Dr. Robert A. Wilson is the leading exponent of estrogen replacement. In his controversial book, *Feminine Forever,* he claims that the menopause is a hormone-deficiency disease that is preventable and curable: [3]

> But when you find a woman of 50 looking like 30, or a woman of 60 looking—and acting—like 40, chances are that she is one of the lucky ones who have benefited from the new techniques of menopause prevention. The outward signs of this age-defying youthfulness are a straight-backed posture, supple breast contours, taut, smooth skin on face and neck, firm muscle tone, and that particular vigor and grace typical of a healthy female. At fifty, such women still look attractive in tennis shorts or sleeveless dresses.
>
> In the course of my work, spanning four decades and involving hundreds of carefully documented clinical cases, it became evi-

dent that menopause—far from being an act of fate or a state of mind—is in fact a deficiency disease. By way of rough analogy, you might think of menopause as a condition similar to diabetes. Both are caused by lack of a certain substance in the body chemistry. To cure diabetes, we supply the lacking substance in the form of insulin. A similar logic can be applied to menopause—the missing hormones can be replaced.

Recent studies indicate that estrogen and testosterone replacement slows the rate of senility in both men and women.

Other Endocrine Glands

The other endocrine glands—the thyroids, the adrenal glands and the pancreas—also play important roles in the aging process. The thyroid hormone controls the rate of body metabolism, and helps prevent arteriosclerosis. As occurs with the gonads, output from the thyroids decreases with age. Though hormonal production by the adrenal glands also declines, there is no evidence to suggest that this decline is a cause of aging. The adrenal glands are important in Dr. Hans Selye's "stress theory" discussed in Chapter 11.

The pancreas produces insulin which controls sugar metabolism. Because the incidence of diabetes increases with age, many elderly people are borderline diabetics. A British scientist, Dr. John Vallance-Owen, in a new theory on the cause of diabetes, estimates that 25 percent of the population has diabetes, a figure that far exceeds the generally accepted incidence rates for the disease.

The old concept of diabetes is that the high sugar levels which characterize the disease result from a lack of insulin. Normal persons, according to the old view, do not have diabetes because their pancreas gland manufactures enough insulin to clear their systems of excess sugar. The new theory, set forth by Vallance-Owen, is that diabetics have a normal quotient of insulin, but they have an excess of a newly discovered substance that deactivates insulin. Diabetics respond to the challenge of this insulin antagonist by making more and more insulin. Eventually the insulin-manufacturing cells become exhausted.

Vallance-Owen found a close correlation between diabetes and heart disease. He gave his test for the presence of the insulin antagonist to a large group of heart attack victims and discovered that by his definition, 65 percent were diabetics. His conclusion was that the diabetic who does not carefully control his disease is also prone to arteriosclerosis.

The findings that an insulin antagonist exists and that its presence has a high correlation with heart disease presents a new insight into the possible causes of heart disease. Also, it points the way to an entirely new way of treating diabetes by means of a drug that lowers the insulin-antagonist level and thus retards the further progress of the disease.

The existence of an insulin antagonist suggests that there may be other hormone-antagonist substances that could better be treated by drugs (blocking agents) than by hormone replacement.

Juvenile Hormone

The life cycles of insects have been significantly changed by "juvenile hormone," a substance which delays maturity without interfering with growth. Continuously injecting juvenile hormone into a silkworm caterpillar prevents it from maturing into the pupa and adult stages. Some investigators report that human placenta, as well as tissue from the thymus and adrenal glands of calves, contain substances similar to juvenile hormone. The possible existence of juvenile hormone in the thymus is of particular significance since this gland is large and active during youth, but almost disappears during adult years. The chemical structure of mammalian juvenile hormone must be unraveled before it can be synthesized, and its possible role in human aging explored.

For many years scientists have speculated on the possible

hormonal role the thymus gland plays in senescence. Like the gonads, the thymus ceases to function as aging progresses. In fact, it is the first gland to atrophy. Its role in developing our immunologic defense system is now well understood. Perhaps it plays an equally important role in producing juvenile hormone. Vertebrates such as the large tortoises, that don't stop growing and do not appear to be affected by the aging process, are perhaps continuously supplied with juvenile hormone. This is all speculation, of course, but the availability of synthetic juvenile hormone might make possible a form of hormone replacement that could completely change our present understanding of endocrine senescence.

The scientist most active in juvenile hormone research, Harvard University's Dr. Carroll M. Williams, points out that juvenile hormone represents, at the insect level, a "Peter Pan hormone." It may contribute to a chemotherapy for aging and Dr. Williams hopefully states that "the day is not too far distant when we will be able to treat senescence as we now know how to treat pneumonia."

The unknown role of mammalian juvenile hormone serves to remind us that there are many undiscovered hormones that serve vital functions in the chemistry of life. Some of them may prove to be important additions to future anti-aging hormone replacement.

The Pituitary Gland and Growth Hormone

The pituitary gland, attached to the brain, is probably the most important gland in the body. It regulates all the other endocrine glands. Evolution has carefully protected it in a bony capsule at the base of the skull. The pituitary produces the gonadotropins that regulate sexual maturity. Most important of all, it produces vital growth hormone which controls the growth of the individual from birth until the full adult size is reached.

Growth hormone, produced throughout the life-span, is

the most powerful anabolic chemical in the body, essential in building new protein. Growth hormone may be the true "juvenile hormone" in mammals. Since its output declines with age, several scientists have suggested that it is the most crucial hormone in mammalian senescence. Alex Comfort observes: [4] "The administration of growth hormone confers strangely youthful proportions on the nitrogen fat and water components of the body, even in old animals, but does not prolong life."

Rats given growth hormone continued to grow after reaching normal adult size. The continued injection of growth hormone, however, had a decreasing effect upon growth and nitrogen retention. However, cattle growth hormone was used, and it has a different molecular structure than rat growth hormone. The increased tissue resistance may be due to the same physiological effects that cause diabetics to become immune to cattle insulin, which has a different molecular structure than human insulin.

Animal growth hormone does not work in humans. Growth hormone research has been severely hindered by the fact that human experiments require growth hormone extracted from human pituitary glands removed at autopsy. Five thousand human pituitary glands will yield only one-sixth of an ounce of human growth hormone. A multimillionaire could not afford growth hormone replacement therapy at the present time.

Human growth hormone was isolated 10 years ago by Dr. Choh Hao Li, the brilliant biochemist who is director of the Hormone Research Laboratory at Berkeley. In 1966 Dr. Li announced that the complete chemical structure of human growth hormone had been deciphered. This hormone (also called somatotrophin) is a complicated chain of 188 amino acids. Once somatotrophin is synthesized, probably in the near future, it will be available in quantity for anti-aging therapy. Understanding the molecular structure of human growth hormone should also enable us to modify animal growth hormone so that it is effective for humans.

It may be possible to proceed with growth hormone replacement without waiting until the chemical substance has been synthesized, by stimulating the pituitary into an increased level of growth hormone secretion. The HCG diet was stressed in Chapter 2 because growth hormone appears to be the physiological basis for this unique means of weight control. As discussed on pages 37–40, HCG causes the hypothalamus to secrete certain chemicals which stimulate the pituitary into increased hormone production.

Some investigators have suggested that excessive growth hormone injections in the adult human induce diabetes. Additional research will be needed to verify this possibility. Perhaps the amount of growth hormone replacement will need to be carefully controlled by some method of measuring growth hormone levels in the body. In any event, the HCG-hypothalamus-pituitary stimulation would not raise growth hormone output to a damaging level.

Growth hormone promises another even more dramatic possibility. We frequently hear of the improvement of human brains by selective breeding (eugenics) or through controlled mutations. Selective breeding would be an administrative nightmare, requiring restraints alien to the way of life in a democratic society. Controlled mutations like selective breeding are reserved for the twenty-first century, beyond the biotechnology expected in the next 20 years. But a recent discovery by UCLA's Dr. Stephen Zamenhof indicates that growth hormone may be capable of creating organisms with superior brains.

Dr. Zamenhof bred rats with bigger brains by injecting growth hormone into pregnant females during that period of the gestation cycle when the brain cells of the unborn fetal rats are still dividing. The growth hormone stimulates the brain cells to divide more often than they normally do. Maze tests indicate that these rats are considerably more intelligent than rats with normal-size brains.

The injection of growth hormone is actually an environmental change, not a genetic modification. When human growth hormone can be synthesized, it could be given to all pregnant women. If Dr. Zamenhof's technique results in the same brain-size increase in humans, with corresponding improved brain power, this revolutionary therapy could produce a race of geniuses.

In addition to growth hormone, Dr. Li's research team discovered other pituitary hormones, including a fat-mobilizing hormone which helps prevent atherosclerosis. Supplemental injections of pituitary fat-dissolving hormones may be useful in the control of obesity and in removing new deposits of cholesterol from arterial walls.

Additional pituitary hormones have yet to be discovered. Their role in daily life processes will no doubt be significant, though their importance in senescence is speculative.

Anti-Aging Hormone Experiments

Many scientists have conducted experiments attempting to extend the life-span of animals by the use of hormones. The anabolic sex steroids caused the animals (primarily rats) to retain a certain degree of youthful appearance and vitality, though the average life-span was no greater than that of the untreated control animals.

Castration, the removal of testicles and ovaries, is an experimental method of withdrawing sex hormones from animals. Castration experiments show that the life-span is not shortened by removing testosterone or estrogen from adult animals. They tend to become obese and inactive, but live as long as fully sexed members of the same species.

The administration of other hormones, including growth hormone, has not extended the life-span of experimental animals. There are many possible hormone replacement experiments that have not been conducted, and it is probable that future research will succeed in achieving some degree of life-span extension through hormone supplementation.

Dr. Clive M. McCay conducted a series of experiments attempting to maintain youthful hormone levels in old animals. He employed a technique called parabiosis, or the artificial creation of Siamese twins. Small rodents were joined surgically side-by-side so that the two animals, now called parabiots, shared a common blood supply. The hormones and all other body chemicals passed back and forth from one animal to the other.

Dr. McCay used a strain of mice that had been so inbred as to constitute virtually a single genetic strain. There were, therefore, no adverse immunological reactions between these mice. Most of the parabiots McCay created were old mice joined to young mice. If aging is caused by hormone imbalance, he reasoned, then theoretically the older members of the parabiot teams should be rejuvenated and have extended life-spans.

The hormones from the young mice did not extend the average life-span of the older mice though the older mice had a more youthful appearance and were more active than non-parabiots of the same age. On the other hand, aging of the young mice was not accelerated by parabiosis. Their life-spans were about the same as the older members of the parabiot teams. When the older mice died, they were surgically removed from their younger companions, allowing the survivors to continue to live.

Though parabiosis is a somewhat radical procedure, and does not represent perfect hormone replacement, it is a useful tool for studying the aging process. McCay's parabiosis experiments have been repeated by other investigators with the same results.

Future Additions to "Elusive Elixir"

Basic research should develop more synthetic additions to our hormonal anti-aging therapy. For instance, it may be possible to locate portions of hormone molecules that have specific biological effects, synthesize those portions and produce therapeutic agents with highly specialized functions.

Though the effects of hormones are well known, the mechanism by which they act has been only vaguely understood. Evidence now indicates that hormones act directly on the basic hereditary material of the genes. They uncover key portions of the genes, and the genes then direct the manufacture of catalytic chemicals (enzymes) which in turn perform a variety of essential life functions. A better understanding of precise biochemical mechanisms of hormonal action within the cells will help define replacement therapy levels and determine the optimum frequency of replacement injections.

Future hormones will probably come from unexpected sources. Some kinds of cancerous tissue manufacture chemicals which act like hormones. Patients with this type of cancer cell do not have the decreased bone density and arthritic changes which usually accompany the aging process. Cancerous tissue has certain similarities to young embryonic tissue. Cancer is a rapidly growing tissue and sometimes seems to create anabolic hormones which rejuvenate bones and possibly even other parts of the body. Such hormones, when it is determined that they do cause cancer, could be used in replacement therapy.

There is strong evidence that some glands produce an excess of certain hormones detrimental to life processes. Excessive thyroid output (hyperthyroidism) is a good example. Though diseases resulting from these excesses are not directly caused by senescence, anything that so increases the body's metabolic activity will affect the aging process. The thyroid is not the only villain. Excessive quantities of adrenalin, cortisone, and other hormones can also be damaging. Specific details will be covered in the review of Dr. Hans Selye's stress theory in Chapter 11.

It should be possible to synthesize chemicals that will suppress hormone output in specific glands. As hormone replacement therapy becomes increasingly sophisticated, these glandular suppression agents may be added to the injections. Such therapy would, however, require continuous monitoring (blood tests, etc.) of each patient so that an optimum internal hormonal balance is maintained.

Hormone replacement therapy is already a reality. It is one of the most effective means presently available of retaining youthful appearance, vitality, sexual potency, and mental alertness. The best current clinical data indicate that optimum benefits occur if the hormone replacement is started relatively early in the life cycle, before there is a serious decline in hormonal output from the ovaries, testicles, etc. Millions of people can benefit though comparatively few men and women are currently receiving continuous hormone injections.

The prospect of vast numbers of people receiving hormone injections means that the present facilities in hospitals, clinics, and physicians' offices would not be adequate to deal with the demand. Pills do not solve the problem because only a few hormones can survive the digestive process in the stomach. The obvious answer is to give the injections at home under careful medical supervision with periodic checks by a physician.

Imaginative technology can make hypodermic injections at home simple, safe and painless if a mass market develops. A new device has been perfected whereby a stream of fluid, under very high pressure, penetrates the skin without a needle injection. The depth of penetration can be varied by altering the pressure. Injections given with this device are almost painless, and can be administered by any untrained person. The present cost for the device is relatively high, but it could be sold for far less if mass-produced.

Clever technological refinement will greatly simplify all aspects of hypodermic injections at home. For example, the hormonal mix could be kept in small custom-filled capsules in a special refrigerator with perfect temperature control. Each day a capsule could be loaded into the automatic pressure device and the revitalizing hormones easily introduced into the body.

We have come a long way since the days of Brown-Séquard, Steinach, and Voronoff. The development of synthetic hormones have supplied many answers. We now know that hormones do not significantly extend the average life-span but are effective in extending the period of youth. Experimental gerontology will continue to refine our use of hormones for anti-aging therapy.

5

~~~~~~~~~~~~~~~~~~~~~~~~~~~~~

Mystery of the Biological Clock

IN RECENT years biologists have begun to study the relationships of living creatures to the time cycles of nature. It has been found out that we are all subject to recurring time cycles —now called "biological clocks." The cyclic physiological responses of any living organism, although influenced by external forces such as magnetic fields, rotation of the earth, darkness and light, is also influenced by internal "clock" mechanisms. The evolutionary process eliminated traits which were not compatible with the environment. Living things adapted their hormone levels, body temperature variations, rest and sleep cycles, reproduction activity and other cyclic responses to their environment so as to assure their survival. Our biological clocks represent the sum total of these physiological and psychological responses. Our circadian rhythm, a complex daily cycle, is one of the most important short-duration biological clocks. The authors of a recent book, *Sleep,* describe how the circadian rhythm influences alertness and sleep: [1]

> A rise and fall of temperature is merely one gauge of the many body cycles that follow a 24-hour period. The heart rate, blood pressure, metabolism, blood cell count, the number of cells dividing in tissue, the volume and chemistry of the urine, kidney

function and many others follow a roughly 24-hour cycle of peaks and lows, many of them in parallel with the temperature. The body chemistry, the composition of blood, the activity of the brain, are different at the time of the bottom temperature than they are during the temperature high.

Biological clocks are an evolutionary phenomena, closely identified with reproduction and survival. The 28-day menstrual cycle is exactly the same as the lunar month. The phases of the moon must have influenced reproduction during millions of years of primate evolution. Again the authors of *Sleep* point out: [2]

> Biological clocks enhance the possibility of survival by putting a creature in tune with the regular changes of nature. The simplest creature without a brain is already pre-set to anticipate approximately the next shift of the outside environment. One California scientist has recorded the spontaneous firing of a single nerve cell in a giant mollusk that is found in tidal pools along the coast. Although the mollusk had been residing in an unchanging tank of seawater in the laboratory, it continued to beat with the tides. The precision of the "clocks" we have found in simple creatures begins to lend some insight into talents they possess, talents once viewed as miraculous.

It has been suggested that the little-understood process of mammalian senescence acts in some fashion as a biological clock, allowing man, under the most favorable circumstances, a life-span rarely extending beyond 90 to 100 years. Are we faced with the mystery of a biological clock of senescence? Is the aging process in mammals something that has been preprogrammed into our genes during millions of years of evolution?

Biological clocks have evolved partly because they play an important role in the survival of the species, though not necessarily the survival of the individual. Some scientists have concluded that aging is a biological clock that deliberately eliminates members of a species when they have completed the functions of reproduction and caring for their young and another cycle of reproduction is begun. Our distant ancestors probably had their children between the ages roughly of 14 and 26 years. By the time they had raised their children to their mid-teens, and taught them to hunt, little more parental protection was needed. At the age of 50, therefore, primitive man would have done all he could to insure the survival of the species. His removal at that point would allow his food to be consumed by younger members.

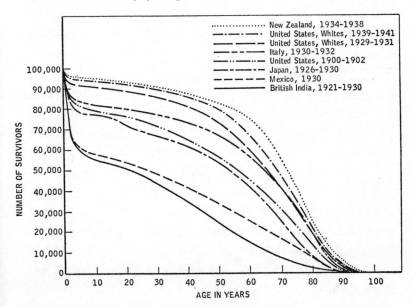

Figure 1. Number of Survivors out of 100,000 Male Live Births. From recent life tables for selected countries taken from *Aging, The Biology of Senescence,* by Alex Comfort, Page 21.

The concept of aging as part of an inevitable biological clock in the "grand design of life" is not new. The ancient Romans, for example, compared life to the descending stream of sand in an hourglass—with even the most fortunate not allotted more than a few extra grains of sand than the average.

The time cycle of the human life-span can be viewed graphically in human survival curves. Figure 1 shows the number of survivors over a 100-year time period.

Figure 1 shows that even in the most adverse environment (India, 1921–1930), some people live to very advanced ages. Note also that the curve begins to level off between the ages of 90 and 100. Of course, this represents only a small portion of the total statistical sample. The curve has not been extended beyond 100 years, because the chart is not large enough to show the few survivors who live beyond one century.

It has been mentioned in Chapter 1 that the birth date records of people who live beyond 100 years are usually questionable. Consequently some gerontological statisticians have concluded that the maximum human life-span is cut off not far beyond 100 years. In fact, some German statisticians in the 1920's dogmatically claimed that their actuarial figures resulted in a human survival curve that "proved" that it was impossible for a man to live beyond 105 years. But such statistical manipulation can give misleading answers. We know that some humans have lived considerably longer than 105 years.

For our immediate purpose of viewing aging as a biological clock, we can set aside age-spans in excess of 100 years. Only between 200 and 300 people out of 100,000 live beyond the century mark in advanced countries and are not, therefore, statistically significant.

Let us consider the survival curve which would result if all major illnesses, including cancer, heart disease and strokes were eliminated. Figure 2 (opposite) shows the expected human survival extension; it would be in the lower portion of the shaded area.

The upper portion of the shaded area is the probable human survival curve if all major disease is eliminated and only modest advances are made in gerontology—principally in the areas outlined in Chapters 2, 3, and 4. It is the expected survival pattern if we would be able to provide people with optimum nutrition, exercise, relaxation, sleep, and hormone replacement. Such advances would result in a more rectangular survival curve, almost flat on top, and falling sharply when the commonest age of senile decline is reached.

If gerontologists can completely decipher the mystery of the biological clock of mammalian senescence, and control or reverse the aging process, a different picture would appear.

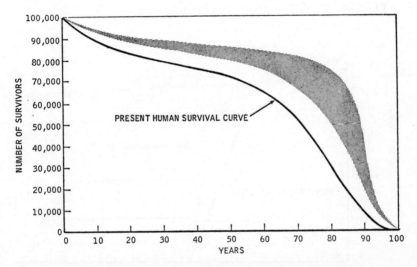

Figure 2. Extension of the Life-Span by Controlling Disease.

The human survival curve would not simply become more rectangular; the entire curve would be shifted to the right, well into the 200-year range. Figure 3 (on page 86) illustrates this exciting prospect.

Figure 3 illustrates the prime purpose of aging research: the goal of significantly extending the life-span of man. Envelope 1 shows the modest gains illustrated in Figure 2. The full understanding and control of the causes of biological aging would mean the human survival curve would fit somewhere into Envelope 2.

The reader may wonder why Figure 3 extends out to the

200-year mark. Experimental gerontology—if adequately funded and supported—should enable man, in this century, to achieve this dramatic extension in the human life-span. The gains may be less or they could be considerably greater. The extent to which the life-span can be actually extended will of course depend on the nature of the aging process itself, on whether the biological clock of senescence will be easily correctable, or very difficult to modify.

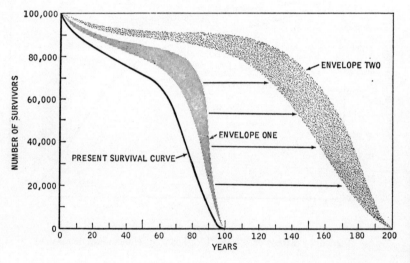

Figure 3. Extension of Life by Controlling the Major Causes of Aging.

Figure 4 (opposite) shows some of the possibilities.

It is possible that we may be able only to slow down biological aging, doubling or tripling the average life-span. However, if there is one major cause of senescence and this is discovered and found to be correctable and completely reversible, the life-span might be greatly extended, perhaps to 500 or 600 years. If every cause of aging can be corrected and prevented, we might all be potential Methuselahs, living 1,000 years or more. Then gerontology would have fulfilled Benjamin Franklin's farsighted prophecy made in 1780:

All diseases may by sure means be prevented or cured, not excepting even that of old age, and our Lives lengthened at pleasure even beyond the Antediluvian Standard.

One unique feature of mammalian aging is that females enjoy longer average life-spans than males. American women, for example, live an average of 3 years longer than American men.

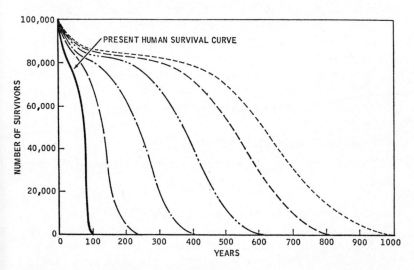

Figure 4. Possible Extension in the Human Life-Span If All Causes of Aging Can Be Corrected.

But it is difficult to determine whether this life-span discrepancy is actually related to the aging process. Nature prepares the female for childbearing, which may also include greater resistance to infectious diseases. It is interesting to note that germ-free male rats live longer than germ-free females.

There is an abundance of theories that attempt to explain the mystery of the biological clock of mammalian senescence. New ones are presented every year. Some are derived from studies of the patterns of senescence in lower forms of life though the aging of amoeba, long-lived trees, and vertebrates, for example, may have nothing in common.

Alex Comfort has concluded that almost all of the contending theories of aging will fit into three main categories or hypotheses: [3]

> Mammals are made up of three biological components: two cellular and one non-cellular. The first two are premitotic cells, such as those of the skin, which are continually dividing, and postmitotic cells, such as the neurones of the brain, which are incapable of division and renewal. The non-cellular material, which includes collagen, may or may not be replaced by new material, according to its location in the body. These three components link with the classical hypotheses of the three mechanisms of ageing, dating from Francis Bacon, but none has yet been investigated by a convincing series of experiments.

Changes in Continuously Dividing Cells

The first category Dr. Comfort describes is based on the thesis [4]

> that vigour declines as a result of changes in the properties of cells which are continually dividing. At present attention is focused on this idea because of its relevance to mutation and the cross-linking of molecules, especially those which carry genetic information. Essentially this hypothesis suggests that new cells in old bodies are not so effective as new cells in young bodies.

By "cross-linking of molecules," Dr. Comfort is referring to the biochemical process by which large molecules, such as DNA, become immobilized as they form chemical bonds with other molecules.

Several theories of aging are based on the mutation hypothesis. One such theory is that mutated cells activate the body's autoimmune mechanism. The body may actually devour itself through the release of antibodies or through some other immunologic reaction (see Chapter 9). Mutated cells are probably less efficient than normal cells in performing their assigned role in the organism. Chapters 8 and 9 will discuss the possible role of mutations in aging.

Changes in, or Loss of Nondividing Cells

Dr. Comfort's second hypothesis is: [5]

... that vigour declines through loss of, or injury to, the non-multiplying postmitotic cells: in other words, irreplaceable cells are lost with time.

The most important of these nonmultiplying cells are in the brain and nerve tissue. The central question is what brings about the changes in fixed cells that causes them to be less efficient or to die. Again there are many explanations. A vertebrate that did not stop growing, such as the giant tortoise, might be continuously replacing essential brain, nerve and other vital cells through continuous cell division.

Chemical cross-linking of genetic DNA and other vital proteins within the fixed cells could cause them to become less efficient. Eventually the accumulating cross-linkages would result in the death of the cell.

The declining vigor and death of fixed cells may also be caused by the intracellular accumulation of toxins. This is an old idea that waste substances are produced faster than the cells can excrete them. Over the years, the residue of waste accumulates to the point where it interferes with the nourishment and vital functioning of the cells, thus causing the deterioration of old age.

The lipofuscin age pigments discussed in Chapter 2 corroborate the "residue interference" explanation. These age pigments occupy between 10 and 30 percent of a cell's total volume. Such debris literally "suffocates" the cell by interfering with the functioning of the molecules responsible for cellular metabolism. There is some evidence that the age pigments are formed by cross-linking.

Chapter 11 will explore the effects of accumulation of calcium, another toxic material, within the fixed cells.

Aging Caused by Noncellular Changes

Let us now look at Dr. Comfort's last category: [6]

> The third hypothesis, that vigour declines through primary changes in the "inert" non-cellular materials of the body, has given rise to extensive and important work on collagen and other components of connective tissue. This is probably the only branch of gerontology widely known to chemists. It revives the old idea that colloid changes form the basis of ageing.

Protein cross-linking is the most plausible explanation of damaging changes in the connective tissue that surrounds the cells of the body. A host of other explanations of aging fit into Comfort's third hypothesis. The "wear-and-tear" theory, for example, states that if a vital organ or tissue is damaged by disease or injury, it never fully recovers. Injury in mammalian tissues frequently leads to fibrosis which means that the organ does not return to an optimum state.

As Alex Comfort points out, however, *"The three grand classical hypotheses of the mechanism of senescence are not mutually exclusive."* [7]

Albert Einstein spent most of his life attempting to devise a "unified field theory" which would explain all the basic forces of physics such as magnetism, gravity, etc. To completely unravel the mystery of the biological clock of mammalian senescence, scientists must devise the biological counterpart of the long sought unified field theory in physics, or what might be termed "a composite theory of aging."

The reader may already have noted that protein cross-linking has a place in all three of Dr. Comfort's hypotheses of senescence. It is possible, therefore, that cross-linking is the nucleus of the true composite theory of aging (see Chapter 13).

We are mammals, and mammals are allowed by nature only one winding of the mysterious clock that determines how long we live. Nature appears to rewind continuously the biological clocks of the sturgeon and giant tortoise. From a theoretical standpoint they could be nearly immortal. The genius of man may soon perfect the anti-aging therapies that will allow our biological clocks to be rewound once, twice, perhaps even indefinitely. Like the sturgeon and tortoise, man is a vertebrate. We only require a means of replacing the descending sands of time in the hourglass of our lives.

In order to determine more precisely the nature of man's relationships to the time cycles of nature and how these relationships can be controlled, it is necessary to investigate in detail the most important theories of mammalian senescence. Each of these theories offers an explanation of the causes of aging and, based on these causes, possible ways to prevent or reverse senescence. It is only by analyzing and sorting out these various explanations—some scientifically sound, some already obsolete—that steps toward a composite theory of aging can be taken.

6

~~~~~~~~~~~~~~~~~~~~~~~~~~~~~~

The Cross-Linkage Theory

A THEORY very likely to be of equal importance to biology as were Albert Einstein's contributions to physics was first refined at the start of World War II by a brilliant chemist, Dr. Johan Bjorksten. Future history books will describe the years of debate, slow acceptance, and the dramatic breakthrough that was the beginning of a true understanding of the aging process.

In 1941, by the age of 34, Johan Bjorksten already had an exceptional education and scientific background in bio-chemistry. At that time he was chief chemist for Ditto, Inc., the world's largest manufacturers of hectograph films. Dr. Bjorksten was exploring means of controlling the elasticity, temperature, diffusion, and swelling characteristics of gelatin gels which are plasticized protein films. He noticed parallels between the behavior of these protein gels and that of human tissues during aging, and noted differences between cross-linked and noncross-linked protein.

In 1941 the initial outline of Dr. Bjorksten's cross-linkage theory of aging was published: [1]

> To those working on this type of precisely regulated tanning, a strange resemblance is apparent between the "aging" of progressive tanning of photographic or of hectograph duplication films, and the aging of the human body. Both processes involve protein reactions, leading to reduced hydration, loss of elas-

ticity; all the earmarks of slowly, but inexorably, progressing tanning reactions.

And the chemist, observing this strange analogy, must wonder if the aging of the human body might not largely, and even principally be an instance of a progressive tanning reaction akin to, or identical with, the "after-hardening" of proteins tanned with a slight trace of aldehyde, in contact with oxygen. The photographic and duplication industries know means of delaying these reactions which are fairly effective, and it does not appear altogether impossible that, at some future time, important contributions towards prolonging the span of human life may emanate from this industrial work.

Within a few months Dr. Bjorksten was able to fully elucidate the cross-linkage theory in what is essentially its form today. In a January 1942 article he stated: [2]

In the living organism, this tanning (cross-linkage) is counteracted by (A)—the directional tanning under influence of repeated stretch and (B)—the continued state of flux in the protein molecules, which are continually split and re-synthesized. In this interplay of synthetic and splitting reactions, the protein molecules are broken down before tanning has gone very far, and re-synthesized in a non-tanned state.

The aging of living organisms I believe is due to the occasional formation, by tanning (cross-linkage), of bridges between protein molecules, which cannot be broken by the cell enzymes. Such irreparable tanning may be caused by tanning agents foreign to the organism, or formed by unusual biological side reactions, or it may be due to the formation of a tanning bridge in some particular position in the protein molecule. In either event, the result is that cumulative tanning of body proteins, which we know as old age.

After World War II, Dr. Bjorksten founded Bjorksten Research Laboratories in Madison, Wisconsin. This organization has since produced many important discoveries and technological refinements for industry and government agencies. However, progress on the cross-linkage explanation of senescence in the postwar years was slow. Government funding agencies had no interest in aging research, especially involving so controversial a concept.

In 1952 the Bjorksten Research Foundation was organized under a nonprofit charter to conduct gerontological research.

In 1951 Dr. Bjorksten restated the cross-linkage theory, along with a proposed anti-aging therapy. He maintained that aging might be controlled by the elimination or control of the chemical agents or conditions causing cross-linking: "Should this procedure prove to be impractical, the desired result might be attained by the development or discovery of a specific enzyme system capable of splitting the causative gerogenic cross-linkages." [3]

The cross-linking explanation of senescence in its final form holds that aging is caused by a gradual but progressive chemical cross-linkage of large vital protein and nucleic acid molecules. These molecules of life are in the shape of long chains or spiral forms. Along the chain there are points which can be chemically linked with molecules by the catalytic action of cross-linking agents. Cross-linking agents act like little rods, with two hooks which link together two giant molecules. During chemical processes within the cell, large molecules are frequently aligned side by side. This is true of nucleic acid DNA as it constructs other giant molecules, when enzymes act on large molecules as in digestion or synthesis, and when chromosomes split lengthwise in cell division and both new chromosomes are lined up side by side. In any of these instances, should a small cross-linking molecule appear and tie the two long molecules together, the long molecules will be incapacitated, in some cases temporarily, in other cases permanently.

Most of the random cross-linkages are harmless since the various enzymes within the body can break them apart. However, a certain percentage are cross-linked in a manner which prevents natural body enzymes from splitting them and these cross-linked molecules can no longer function normally. As this process continues, the vital proteins and nucleic acid molecules are bound together in pairs and even larger aggregates which are irreversibly immobilized. The resulting accumulation of this "frozen metabolic pool" clogs the cells, interferes with the functioning of the remaining free molecules, and ultimately destroys the cells.

The cross-linking effect may be likened to what would happen in a large factory with thousands of workers if someone slipped a pair of handcuffs on one hand of each of two workers to bind them together. This obviously would reduce their ability to do their work, and if the process were allowed to spread through the factory, even at a slow rate, it would ultimately paralyze the entire operation unless means were found to remove the handcuffs faster than they were being applied.

A cell is particularly vulnerable to cross-linkage when in a state of division or high biological activity. By the very nature of the chromosome mechanism and replications, there cannot be duplicates in the cell, for these might interfere with each other. If the key molecules are destroyed, immobilized, or modified by cross-linkages, the cell either dies or, if there is only one cross-linkage, there might be a rupture which leads to mutations, mostly of functionally inferior cells.

The body is full of cross-linking agents. A potential cross-linker is a molecule with two or more exposed sites that have either a deficiency or a surplus of electrons. These electrons react with supplementary sites on giant molecules, of which many are formed by the body's normal metabolic processes. Some are compounds of undesirable trace elements including lead, aluminum and copper. Necessary trace elements (iron, manganese, zinc) also form cross-linking compounds. Other typical cross-linkers include:

Acetaldehyde	Malic acid	Alpha-ketoglutaric acid
Glyceraldehyde	Kynurenic acid	Pyruvic acid
Pyruvaldehyde	Succinic acid	Citric acid

It should be noted that a high percentage of cross-linking agents in the body are intermediate products that accumulate when more food is consumed than can be utilized immediately; another reason for the life-shortening effects of overeating.

Radiation produces cross-linking agents. When gamma rays, neutrons, and other forms of radiation pass through the body, part of their energy is transferred to individual atoms in the tissues. A low-energy transfer produces heat. A high-energy transfer strips some of the electrons from the outer shell of the atom, forming a short-lived particle called an ion. This process of creating electrically charged atoms is called ionization. The ion moves from its original position and quickly corrects its electron deficiency, often by binding together protein molecules. Ions frequently create other short-lived substances called free radicals. They are unstable molecular fragments which last only a few thousandths of a second. A free radical has free valence electrons and it will quickly bind itself to suitable molecules within the cells, causing cross-linking and other forms of damage.

Free radicals are also formed in the body by normal metabolic processes. These free radicals and those formed by ionizing radiation are the most powerful cross-linkers in the body.

The carbon monoxide in tobacco smoke causes cross-linking chemicals to accumulate. Tobacco smoke contains other specific cross-linking agents. Calciphylaxis (Chapter 11) may also play a part since calcium is bivalent and therefore a potential cross-linking agent. Antibodies from autoimmune reactions (Chapter 9) may also cause cross-linking.

While the body continues to grow, cells are dividing and the accumulating cross-linked material is being evenly distributed between the new cells and in the expanding connective tissue between the cells. When growth stops, the amount of cross-linked material in the body continues to expand and occupies, by volume, more and more space in the tissues. This would explain why vertebrates that continue to grow do not appear to age. Though they have an increasing quantity of insoluble cross-linked material in their bodies, the volume of their new cells and connective tissue is growing at a faster rate than the volume of the cross-linked material.

Now we can understand Clive McCay's rat experiments. His underfeeding brought the growth of the rats almost to a halt. The growth phase was prolonged past the time period of a normal rat life-span. Also, they had so little caloric food that it was quickly metabolized, with fewer cross-linking agents produced as intermediate products in food metabolism.

The cross-linkage theory also explains Alexis Carrel's classic observation in 1911 that cultured cells appear to perpetuate themselves indefinitely. There is an almost total absence of cross-linking agents in the nutrient used to maintain tissue cultures. In fact, a completely synthetic mixture of specific amino acids, vitamins, minerals, essential fatty acids, and glucose are often used to maintain tissue cultures. Any cross-linkages resulting from free radicals or other causes would be absorbed by cell division. The volume of the tissue culture would be growing significantly faster than the mass of cross-linked material.

Independent Confirmation of Bjorksten's Theory

The cross-linkage theory was proposed independently by three different scientists working in three different areas without knowledge of each other's work. Bjorksten was the first by over 15 years. He evolved the theory in perhaps the most difficult manner—from a study of chemistry. In early 1956, Dr. Frederic Verzár deduced the theory from studies in physiology. In 1959 Dr. Donald G. Carpenter formulated the theory from studies of nuclear science and radiation effects. This independent confirmation suggests that the cross-linkage theory is a highly plausible explanation of the aging process.

Frederic Verzár is a remarkable Hungarian scientist who

moved to Switzerland in 1930. His scientific accomplishments were already varied and distinguished when he became interested in experimental gerontology in 1952. Dr. Verzár retired from the University of Basel in 1956 at the age of 70 and founded *Gerontologia,* a journal devoted exclusively to papers on experimental gerontology. In 1956 he moved his animal colony and equipment into a new laboratory and continued his research on aging. Progress was rapid and on January 1, 1959, the Foundation for Experimental Gerontology was organized.

In 1956 Dr. Verzár had concluded that the cross-linking of collagen, a substance which constitutes 40 percent of all the protein in the body, may play an important role in senescence. In 1965 Dr. Verzár and Dr. Holger P. von Hahn were able to demonstrate the phenomenon of an increasing amount of irreversible binding of protein to DNA in aging thymus cells. Current research at the Foundation may soon demonstrate direct DNA-RNA cross-linking. Dr. Verzár speculates that "only those macromolecules (large) which are not renewed during life show aging and may be cross-linked as aging collagen is."

Dr. Verzár and Dr. Bjorksten began to communicate with each other and exchange research data. At the International Congress of Gerontology in August 1963, held in Copenhagen, Dr. Verzár publicly gave Dr. Bjorksten full credit for having initiated the cross-linking theory of senescence. At that same meeting, Dr. Nathan W. Shock said that the aging theories that seemed most plausible were the ones of somatic mutations (Chapter 8) and the cross-linkage theory.

It is interesting to note that, in 1960, Dr. Shock published a paper [4] listing ten criteria which any valid theory of aging would have to meet. In 1962, in another paper,[5] Dr. Bjorksten showed that the cross-linking theory satisfied all of Dr. Shock's criteria and then presented three additional criteria.

Major Donald G. Carpenter, a research associate in the Department of Physics at the U.S. Air Force Academy in

Colorado, independently deduced the cross-linkage theory while studying the effects of ionizing radiation on living tissue. Dr. Carpenter believes that cross-linkage applies to all molecules in the body, not just to proteins and amino acids. He has conducted [6] some ingenious computer experiments which provide mathematical evidence that the age pigments in human heart cells appear as a result of cross-linkage. Dr. Carpenter has also demonstrated that the behavior of accumulated cross-linked material is in accord with our present understanding of diffusion phenomena in the body—additional evidence for the cross-linkage theory.

Cross-Linkage in Various Tissues

Dr. Bjorksten and his colleague Dr. Howard Gottlieb have some preliminary experimental evidence that arteriosclerosis is caused by a series of steps initiated by cross-linkage. The first step in arteriosclerosis is a small rupture in the endothelium tissue which lines the interior artery walls. These small ruptures may be caused by cross-linkage which makes a small portion of the endothelium tissue rigid or "brittle" and subject to cracking during the pulsation cycles of the arterial system. Blood serum then filters through the rupture, depositing suspended materials such as cholesterol particles.

Dr. H. H. Zinsser at Columbia University found evidence of cross-linking in aging human aorta tissue. He devised a unique new method to examine complex samples using X-ray diffraction techniques.

In one remarkable experiment Fred Andrews, a longtime associate of Dr. Bjorksten, and Dr. Bjorksten found lipofuscin age pigments in the heart cells of stillborn babies. They also demonstrated that there is a considerable amount of insoluble cross-linked material in the heart muscle of older humans. They used hearts obtained at autopsy from males ranging in age from 64 to 74 years.

Dr. Bjorksten also has obtained strong evidence that the

aging of human skin is caused in large measure by the cross-linking effects of ultraviolet radiation.

In 1966 a special book, *Perspectives in Experimental Gerontology,* was prepared in honor of Frederic Verzár's 80th birthday. Thirty distinguished gerontologists from many countries contributed to this important scientific compendium. Never before had so much evidence been assembled in support of the cross-linkage theory, including chapters describing the cross-linking of collagen, elastin, and DNA.

Corrective Therapy for Cross-Linking

How can we prevent or reverse the damage caused by cross-linking agents? The most immediate step is a low-caloric, high-protein diet. A low-caloric intake would assure a rapid metabolic combustion process, producing harmless end products of carbon dioxide and water. The intermediate metabolites, which can cause cross-linkage, would thereby be processed quickly. The high-protein portion of the diet would maintain a high content of free amino acids. These aminos draw off some of the intermediates which would otherwise cross-link proteins or nucleic acids (DNA and RNA).

Dietary restriction is not, however, the solution to cross-linking. At best it offers a modest life-span extension. Synthetic food, by eliminating nonessential trace elements that cause cross-linkages, would be superior to natural food in aging retardation. Also the metabolism of synthetic food produces fewer intermediate metabolites.

Johan Bjorksten has proposed a therapy to counteract cross-linkage. He suggests breaking down all the cross-linked molecule groups with enzymes. These groups could then be excreted from the cell, thereby freeing this space for the synthesis of new, noncrossed-linked molecules produced by normal cell processes. The enzymes would not need to break the cross-linkages themselves, but rather reduce the cross-linked molecules to small excretable fragments. The normal proteins also attacked by the enzymes would be replaced by normal synthesis in the cell provided the enzymes were administered at a sufficiently slow rate. As a result of this therapy, the cells would be restored to a more active state, and the organism would be partly rejuvenated.

Dr. Bjorksten suggests certain specific enzymes for these procedures: [7] "An elastase or some other enzyme already known, properly used, could be quite effective. A larger range of substances would be found by investigation of soil bacteria. The technique used by R. Dubos for other purposes might be adapted: to prepare a highly cross-linked protein or nucleic acid material which cannot be broken down with any known enzyme, wash out and digest out of it all soluble material and make the remaining hard-core substance the only energy source or the only nitrogen source in a culture of mixed soil bacteria. Only organisms capable of breaking down the cross-linked material could then survive. Once an organism capable of breaking down the cross-linked material has been found, we are on a promising trail. Much research would still be needed to grow the organism in quantity, extract the enzymes and find a way of bringing them into all cells (possibly as precursors), but after many false starts and heartbreaks with toxic or otherwise unsuitable products we *might* end up with a product of therapeutic utility."

Many thousands of different strains of soil bacteria would probably have to be investigated before an enzyme rejuvenating "elixir" was found. Therefore, it would be necessary to prepare a large quantity of cross-linked material that couldn't be broken down by normal body enzymes. Dr. Bjorksten used a low temperature chemical, anhydrous hydrogen fluoride, as a solvent to isolate the cross-linked material. The processing is conducted at temperatures as low as $-83°$ C. Anhydrous hydrogen fluoride could also be used for a large-scale isolation of sizable quantities of cross-linked material.

Cross-linking agents added to tissue cultures would alter

their growth characteristics. Soil bacteria enzymes and other enzymes then introduced to the culture should indicate which of these enzymes break down the cross-linkages, thereby enabling the tissue cultures to resume their characteristic growth pattern.

A truly adequate anti-aging research program should uncover several means of breaking up cross-linked protein and nucleic acids. The stimulation of certain natural enzyme mechanisms is very promising. For example, collagen cross-linkages occur in the uterus during pregnancy. After pregnancy, the cross-linkage bonds are broken. Another example occurs in lathyrism, a disease known for almost 100 years and encountered mainly in India and Spain during times of famine when the main diet consists of the chick-pea *Lathyrus sativus*. The disease involves destruction of collagen in the body by a chemical known as B-aminopropionitrile. Other chemicals produce effects similar to lathyrism. These include certain ureides and hydrazines, niacin hydrazide being one of the most potent.

Lathyrism-inducing chemicals do not destroy already cross-linked collagen, but prevent cross-linkage in young collagen just being formed. Unless extreme caution is used in the dosage, the collagen which forms a part of the bones is also attacked, and the bones become extremely brittle. If, however, these agents are carefully controlled, it should be possible to keep the rate of decomposition below the rate of resynthesis so that replacement and renewal of the collagen-based fibrils is achieved without danger. The monitoring of the rate of collagen decomposition or remobilization of ancient collagen in the body can be done by controlling the amount of hydroxyproline in the urine, a by-product of collagen breakdown or synthetic activity. Investigators have recently found that penicillamine also prevents the formation of excessive amounts of insoluble collagen in rats.

The possibility of triggering new enzyme formation presents a number of promising research options. Certain proteins, or protein decomposition products not normally present, may stimulate the production of beneficial enzymes.

Aging therapy and treatments for other medical problems would greatly benefit from a better understanding of the molecular structure of enzymes. Once the specific portions of enzyme molecules that cause desirable biological reactions can be identified and synthesized, artificial enzymes can be produced. These might even prove superior to natural enzymes in breaking down cross-linked material.

Dr. Linus Pauling stresses the importance of enzymes: [8]

> The problem of enzymes encompasses essentially the whole of biology. When we understand enzymes—their structure, the mechanism of their synthesis, the mechanism of their action— we shall understand life, except for those aspects of life that involve mental processes; and I have no doubt that enzymes are important for these too.

> Enzymes do an extraordinary job—that of causing chemical reactions to take place in the body, at body temperature, which without enzymes can be made to take place only under much different conditions or with great difficulty. The outstanding characteristic of enzymes is their specificity. For example, the enzyme B-galactosidase is able easily to hydrolyse a galactoside, where it has little effect on hydrolysis of a glucoside, which differs from the galactoside only in the spatial configuration about a single carbon atom.

Some Additional Considerations

Once suitable enzymes are available in quantity, we will be faced with the problem of getting them into the cells. Temperature and pressure are two important though neglected environmental parameters in biological research. Indeed temperature may be the key to enzyme therapy since enzymes are highly sensitive to temperature. It might be necessary to reduce the body temperature to the point where the enzymes could be effectively introduced into the body. Perhaps it would only be necessary to keep the body at a low temperature until the enzymes were able to penetrate all the cells.

Enzyme therapy might resemble the following pattern: (1) The body temperature would be lowered below the point where the enzymes are effective so they could be introduced and distributed uniformly throughout all body tissues. (2) The body temperature would be raised to the point where the enzymes could break down cross-linked material. (3) The body temperature would then be raised to normal. This would destroy or inactivate the enzymes, thus switching off the reaction before it could cause any damage.

The demands on the enzyme system are fewer at a reduced metabolic temperature, inasmuch as adverse side reactions are reduced. The beneficial hydrolysis at a controlled rate could be enhanced at some optimum temperature determined by simple animal experiments. Both hibernating and nonhibernating animals might be used in experiments. The polyethylene intubation technique described in Chapter 10 is one possible means of introducing the enzymes into their systems.

Another possible method is hypothermia, a technique widely used in clinical medicine to reduce tissue and overall body metabolic requirements prior to surgery. Hypothermia is different from natural hibernation. Hypothermia is artificially inducted cooling by exposing an animal to a lower than normal body temperature, while natural hibernation is an intrinsic cooling programmed and controlled by the animal itself. The naturally hibernating animal is able to lower its body temperature to 3 or 4 degrees above the freezing point of water without undergoing a fluttering or ineffective beating of the heart called fibrillation. When a nonhibernating animal (or hibernating animal which is not biochemically prepared for hibernation) experiences a body temperature reduction to as low as 65–68° F, its heart develops fibrillation. This fibrillation has been a serious drawback both in clinical hypothermia and in the research for mechanism behind artificial hibernation.

The fibrillation problem has been solved by Dale L. Carpenter, a brilliant and innovative space biologist. His research utilized both hibernating and nonhibernating animals to gain an insight to the comparison of the physiology of natural hibernation and artifically induced hypothermia. He determined that probably the same basic temperature control exists both in hibernating and nonhibernating mammals, and were a nonhibernating mammal to be biochemically prepared with proper enzymes and energy-producing biochemicals, it could also hibernate. Biochemical and energy-producing chemicals would be utilized with cyclic cooling to induce the artificial hibernation.

Cyclic hypothermia is the unique new concept which prevents heart fibrillation. Hypothermia is induced until the heart just begins quivering, at which point the animal is rewarmed to normal body temperature by diathermy. After an interval of time, the process is repeated. Utilizing this method, Dale L. Carpenter found that after each cooling, the temperature at which the heart quivered (fibrillated) was progressively lower. That is, the first fibrillation temperature might be 68° F and the heart would not fibrillate on the second cold exposure until the body had been cooled to 65° F. Each exposure appeared to set up a conditioning process which caused the heart to be less susceptible to failure. Such techniques might well be used to modify the action or change the balance of hormones, and otherwise provide biochemical changes that would affect the aging of cells and the whole organism.

When perfected, artificial hibernation will be useful in enzyme therapy. Scientists studying hibernation are refining techniques involving the use of hibernation-inducing biochemicals given in a process similar to intravenous feeding. When the scientists are successful, man could become an artificial hibernator. To duplicate natural hibernation, we must thoroughly understand its physiology, the subtle changes in endocrine hormone balance, key enzyme processes, energy storage and utilization, and their synergistic interrelationships.

The diffusion of corrective enzymes into the cells would

however, be hindered by the cross-linked material outside of the cells. Dimethyl sulfoxide (DMSO), which acts as a "carrier solute," might be effective in facilitating intracellular enzyme penetration. If DMSO is too toxic at the body temperature needed for optimum diffusion of the enzymes, fluorinated or deuterized chemical variants of DMSO could be synthesized (hydrogen atoms replaced with fluorine or heavy hydrogen atoms) to counteract the toxicity.

Enzyme rejuvenation therapy is, of course, still speculative. Probably cross-linked material in the arteries and connective tissue would be broken down before the enzymes could effectively penetrate to the vital fixed cells of the body.

Dr. Bjorksten's anti-aging enzymes could also be used to reverse many of the damaging, often fatal, effects of nuclear radiation since the damaging mechanism of ionizing radiation lies in the formation of free radicals that cause cross-linkage and destroy vital DNA.

The cross-linking aging theory is difficult to prove without actually observing the effects on the aging process of the breakdown of the body's cross-linked material. It is conceivable that a crash program, mobilizing the research resources of the entire pharmaceutical industry, could be successful in five years. In addition to searching for new soil bacteria enzymes, this program could begin animal experiments with known agents that break down cross-linked material.

However, revolutionary theoretical approaches, such as the cross-linkage theory, seldom receive adequate funding until collaborative evidence begins to come from many laboratories. Dr. Bjorksten has spent over $60,000 of his own money on cross-linkage research since 1952. Government funding includes $36,841 from the Office of Naval Research, $15,000 from the Air Force Office of Scientific Research, and $12,409 from the U.S. Atomic Energy Commission. The J. M. Foundation donated $52,500.

Between 1955 and 1965, many scientists provided collaborative evidence in support of the cross-linkage theory. In 1966 the Upjohn Company of Kalamazoo, Michigan, appropriated $250,000 for a five-year research program on cross-linkage with the Bjorksten Research Laboratories. The far-sighted management decision of this pharmaceutical company marked the point of full recognition of the cross-linkage theory, 25 years after it was first proposed. Such a time lag is not unusual in the biological sciences. The American Nobel Laureate Dr. John H. Northrop observes: [9]

> The history of biochemistry is a chronicle of a series of controversies, in several of which I have been more or less engaged. These controversies exhibit a common pattern. There is a complicated hypothesis, which usually entails an element of mystery and several unnecessary assumptions. This is opposed by a more simple explanation, which contains no unnecessary assumptions. The complicated one is always the popular one at first, but the simpler one, as a rule, eventually is found to be correct. This process frequently requires 10 to 20 years. The reason for this long time lag was explained by Max Planck. He remarked that scientists never change their minds, but eventually they die.

Max Planck (1858–1947) first presented the quantum theory of physics in 1900, for which he was awarded the Nobel Prize in 1918. However, there was a long time lag before acceptance and full understanding when, in the 1920's, Sir George Thomson and other scientists made discoveries fundamental to the quantum theory.

Bjorksten's theory is the simple explanation of aging which promises to displace more complicated hypotheses. The cross-linkage theory treats senescence as an intracellular phenomenon—the result of the cross-linking of molecules within individual cells which immobilizes these cells. With the viability of the cross-linkage phenomenon established, scientists can now apply it to certain of the more significant manifestations of aging.

7

~~~~~~~~~~~~~~~~~~~~~~~~~~~~~~~

Connective Tissue and Collagen

ONE of the oldest and most enduring hypotheses in gerontology is that mammalian aging is primarily caused by changes
in the connective tissue of the body. The connective tissues
are those which bind together, connect and support other
tissues. Bone, cartilage, tendons, ligaments, for example, and
the loose irregularly arranged cells which line the skin and
occupy spaces between other organs are composed primarily
of connective tissue. Scar tissue is a local deposit of connective
tissue. The connective tissues maintain their own structure and
produce blood cells, fat cells, and other cells which are active
in the repair of wounds. These cells are surrounded by three
types of fibrous protein molecules—collagen, elastin, and re-
ticulin. The connective tissue cells and fibrous molecules are
all imbedded in an amorphous jellylike material called ground
substance.

More than half of the body is composed of connective tissue.
Obese people have a higher percentage of connective tissue
than slender people because adipose tissue is composed largely
of cells in which fat is stored.

Connective tissue undergoes significant changes as we age.
Senescence is characterized by the loss of vital, nonregenerating

cells in the brain, heart, kidneys, etc., which tend to be replaced by fibrous connective tissue.

In summary, the connective tissues perform a mechanical function, holding the body together and supporting the organs. All the fluids and hormones in the body must pass through the connective tissues. The fat cells serve as a depository or reserve, supplying the body with energy and stored vitamins when nutritional intake is reduced. The cells in the connective tissue also play a vital role in the body's repair and defensive mechanisms.

Sometimes the term "connective tissue" is used without specifying which component (fibrous protein, ground substance, or cells) is being considered. When analyzing the aging process, care should be taken to mention the component of connective tissue that is the subject of consideration.

Prior to the 1950's, research into the relationship between connective tissue and aging was channeled in misleading directions. Although we know today that these exotic therapies the early researchers proposed are not valid, their investigations and applications paved the way for the more responsible scientific research that followed, and which resulted in certain important breakthroughs in our understanding of the aging process.

Bogomoletz's Theory and ACS Serum

From 1941 until 1953, a great deal of publicity was given to a sensational theory of aging that came from the Soviet Union. Dr. Alexander Alexandrovitch Bogomoletz, the president of the Ukrainian Academy of Sciences and founder-director of the Kiev Institute of Experimental Biology and Pathology, maintained that the connective tissues play the major role in aging. Even more dramatic was his announcement of a rejuvenation serum that would delay the aging process.

Bogomoletz's theory has its roots in the early 1900's, when

the great Russian bacteriologist Dr. Ilya Metchnikoff (1845–1916) began his efforts to unravel the riddle of aging. He discovered phagocytosis, the body's defense against invading bacteria by means of white blood cells (phagocytes) which devour the offending foreign bodies. In 1908, he was awarded the Nobel Prize for this significant discovery.

Metchnikoff's theoretical speculation evolved in a rather odd way, and resulted in an unorthodox conclusion. By a roundabout pattern of reasoning, he theorized that aging is largely caused by bacterial toxins produced in the large intestine and that these toxins poisoned brain and nerve cells so that they became weakened and subject to destruction by scavenger phagocytes.

Metchnikoff proposed two anti-aging therapies: to have the colon (large intestine) surgically removed or to alter its bacterial content. For the latter approach he recommended yogurt, a form of sour milk that contained, in large quantity, lactobacillus bulgaricus, a lactic-acid-producing organism. He believed that a high yogurt diet would make the colon's content too acidic for the toxin-producing bacteria to survive. As proof, he cited the examples of Bulgarian peasants who consumed large quantities of yogurt and were reported to enjoy significantly long life-spans.

It is not surprising that Metchnikoff created a worldwide demand for yogurt, previously a Balkan and Near Eastern milk product. Though yogurt is a nutritious food, it has no effect on acidity in the colon or on senescence.

Almost 60 years have passed since Metchnikoff started the yogurt craze. The longevity of false rejuvenation proposals can be seen in the fact that one frequently hears that "yogurt" will maintain youth.

In recent years biomedical research has proven that the bacteria in the large intestine are harmless. People who have had their colon removed (usually because of cancer) do not live longer than average. Germ-free animals with no bacteria in their colons do not have exceptional life-spans.

Alexander Bogomoletz (1881–1946) was a student of Metchnikoff. Dr. Bogomoletz reinterpreted some of his teacher's earlier speculations on the role of connective tissue in the aging process. He concluded that the structure and condition of the cells of the connective tissue determine the human organism's resistance to changes accompanying the aging process, such as hardening of the arteries, arthritis, and other degenerative diseases. Sir William Osler's "a man is as old as his arteries" was paraphrased by Bogomoletz: "Man is as old as his connective tissue." Actually Bogomoletz included in his definition of connective tissue all the cells in the reticuloendothelial system, including cells in the spleen, lymph nodes, bone marrow, endothelial linings of vital organs and glands as well as noncellular constitutents.

Bogomoletz concluded that adverse changes in the reticuloendothelial system are caused by the death of the cells and their replacement by fibrous tissue. Consequently, the body gradually loses flexibility, adaptability, and the capacity to fight infection and injury. The increased fiber "suffocates" the surrounding cells of organs and glands. Nutrients and hormones are no longer adequately transported by reticuloendothelial cells to all the other cells of the body. The result is a form of cellular starvation.

Bogomoletz believed that he had conclusively confirmed his theory in the late 1930's after exhaustive physical examinations and postmortems were performed on Caucasus centenarians, whose ages ranged from 107 to 135 years. He noted that the network of elastic tissue forming the inner and outer lining of their organs was invariably in a remarkable state of preservation.

In June 1941, Bogomoletz announced the refinement of a serum to strengthen the cells of the reticuloendothelial system.

It was called Anti-Reticular Cytotoxic Serum—usually referred to as "ACS serum." Bogomoletz's approach was based on the observation that certain toxins, in small quantities, strengthen certain tissues while larger quantities of the same substance kill the tissues.

Human spleen cells and marrow cells from the sternum were taken from the corpses of young men killed in accidents and were then injected into horses. The horse's blood was removed and the serum with its specific antibodies separated out. Both the spleen and sternum marrow cells, part of the reticuloendothelial system, are rich in connective tissue. The active components in ACS serum were the antibodies against spleen and marrow tissue, which in small doses might have a stimulating effect on the reticuloendothelial system, though large doses could paralyze and destroy vital connective tissue.

Hailed as a rejuvenating elixir 25 years ago, it failed to live up to all the sensational reports and was labeled a hoax. Stalin took the serum, and his death at 73 did not help the cause of this controversial treatment. The very month Stalin died (March 1953), there were American magazine articles suggesting that ACS serum would enable Stalin to live 100 years or more though it was not known whether Stalin had only a few ACS shots or had been taking it for several years. Alexander Bogomoletz had a heart condition which prevented him from taking ACS serum himself. His death at the relatively early age of 65 in 1946 is often mentioned by his detractors.

But Bogomoletz never said that his serum would actually rejuvenate, only that it would slow down the aging process: [1]

> Hope for the prolongation of life should not be pinned on attempts to rejuvenate an organism that is old. It is hard to turn back the river current. But to slow down the process of exhaustion of the organism's functions, the process of aging, is possible by the wise control of one's life.

Bogomoletz suggested that ACS serum might be of value as an aging preventative rather than a rejuvenation serum: [2]

If it should prove that the small doses of the anti-reticular cyto-toxic serum, on repeated introduction into the body are able to prevent untimely sclerosis of the reticulo-endothelial system, this serum will become a very valuable aid in the struggle for prolongation of life. We have begun to study this problem. Here a great deal of circumspection and long experimentation first on animals and later on human beings is needed. . . . But it is also possible that, through a prolonged cytotoxic stimulation, the connective tissue will excessively proliferate and then become sclerotic. The question of proper dosage will be of decisive importance.

Very little has been written about ACS serum since Stalin died though it is still manufactured in Germany and also admin-istered in Mexico.

The disappointing results of ACS serum therapy does not completely disprove Bogomoletz's basic theory that resistance to disease and the degenerative processes of aging are con-trolled by connective tissue cells. Like Voronoff, Bogomoletz was a pioneer who made a daring attempt to control aging and whose basic ideas still supply valuable information to the now broader study of senescence.

There is one more individual in the reticuloendothelial cast. Dr. Alexander Bogomoletz had a cousin, Dr. Victor Bogomo-letz, a physician, who accepted all of his famous cousin's aging theory, except that he suggested a modified therapy. Victor believed that accurate dosages of ACS serum would be difficult to determine. Instead, he proposed to stimulate the body's connective tissue and organs by means of substances absorbed through the skin—"rejuvenation through externotherapy."

Though externotherapy has little scientific basis, the reader may find the details interesting. Victor Bogomoletz considered the skin an endocrine gland. And since it is composed pri-marily of connective tissue, Alexander Bogomoletz's theories applied. Victor paraphrased his cousin's maxim saying: "We are as old as our skin."

He traced the origin of externotherapy to the Caucasus: [3]

> In the Caucasus, and in Persia particularly, we have noticed
> that various illnesses are cured by the application to the patient's
> body of skins of animals removed immediately after death. It is
> interesting at this point to quote a method used by the peasants
> in the Caucasian Mountains: wild animals are beaten for several
> days, the skin is then taken off and applied to people suffering
> from rheumatism. Let us remember also here Filatov and his
> discovery as to how cells which are "suffering" give off positive
> substances possessing a rare power, substances which are also
> soluble in water.

Victor Bogomoletz believed that when cells degenerate,
rejuvenating substances are formed—an observation of his
cousin Alexander who had said: "The products of the tissue's
disintegration act like hormones or more correctly . . . as auto-
catalysts (enzymes that digest or otherwise modify cells similar
to the cells that produce them)." Victor Bogomoletz proposed
to introduce these substances through the skin after it was
properly prepared. In his summary of externotherapy he said: [4]

> It remains for medical science . . . to find these substances and
> stimulants and to make them absorbable . . . it is now accept-
> able to regard the skin itself as an endocrine gland; the existence
> of functional relationships between all the endocrine glands
> allows the discharge, from the skin, of chemical messengers
> which excite the different endocrinal changes, modify the me-
> tabolism, and influence the secretory condition of the cells.
> Finally, the pituitary, the main endocrine gland, centralizes all
> the endocrinal stimuli and transmits a balance to the nervous
> system.

The quackery of externotherapy is confirmed by its association with "other branches of applied medicine such as cosmo-
biology, hydrotherapy, electrotherapy, actinotherapy, homo-
lotherapy, and 'acupuncture' (the latter is externotherapy par
excellence)." [5]

Victor Bogomoletz operated an externotherapy clinic in
Paris for many years. Since the emphasis was on the skin, it is

not surprising that almost all his patients were women. Nothing has been heard of his treatment since the 1950's.

For the first half of this century, efforts to determine the role of connective tissue in senescence have been diverted into false channels—yogurt, ACS serum, and externotherapy. Only since about 1950 has responsible research begun to elucidate the causes of the changes in connective tissue that occur as the body ages.

Molecular Changes in Connective Tissue

The cells and fibrous protein molecules of connective tissue are embedded in ground substance, a jellylike material most often consisting of five chemicals called mucopolysaccharides. With age, this material decreases in volume as the amount of collagen increases. The chemical composition of the remaining ground substance also changes. One component (mucopolysacch chondroitin sulfate) decreases from 6 percent of the dry weight of cartilage at birth, to less than 1 percent at age 75. The "4-sulfate form" of chondroitin sulfate in the tissues is replaced by the "6-sulfate form." By the time a human reaches the age of 50, only the 6-sulfate form is present.

Dr. Karl Meyer of Columbia University discovered that ground substance loses 50 to 70 percent of its hyaluronic acid by the time a person reaches the age of 70. It appears that hyaluronic acid acts as a lubricant for the elastin molecules in connective tissue. Loss of this lubricant decreases the flexibility of elastin. Since hyaluronic acid also has an ability to retain water in the connective tissues, its decreasing quantity results in water loss, partly accounting for wrinkles and the increased fiber content that characterizes mammalian senescence.

There is a definite need for some well-directed research aimed at determining the causes of ground substance age changes and the means of restoring ground substance to an optimum state. It is significant that vertebrates which continue to grow do not exhibit comparable changes in the ground substance of their connective tissues.

Elastin is a rubbery, noncrystalline, elastic molecule, one of the two important protein fibers in connective tissue. Elastin gives blood vessels, lung tissue, elastic ligaments, and other parts of the body their flexibility. Elastin becomes less flexible with age. There has been some speculation that this is caused by an increased amount of calcium in the system (Chapter 11).

The volume of elastin in the connective tissue also decreases with age and is replaced largely with cross-linked collagen. Elastin fibers break up into smaller pieces (possibly caused by mechanical stress) and change from a light yellow to a darker yellow.

There is mounting evidence that age-related changes in elastin are caused by cross-linkages. In fact, elastin appears to be much more susceptible to cross-linkage damage than collagen. Relatively few cross-linkages will radically alter the physical characteristics of elastin.

Many of the changes in ground substance as it ages also appear to be caused by cross-linking.

Collagen

More is known about the aging of collagen (a gelatinous substance found in connective tissue, bone and cartilage) than about any other protein in the body. With age, a great deal of vital elastin and ground substance is replaced by collagen which becomes increasingly cross-linked. This cross-linkage is extremely important because collagen constitutes between 30 and 40 percent of the body protein.

Frederic Verzár has described the importance of collagen: [6]

> Collagen supplies the matrix in which the calcium salts that give the bones their hardness are deposited. Collagen is the substance of cartilage and tendon; it fills up the spaces between muscle fibers and between the cells of many organs serving as

the stabilizing fiber of connective tissue. In the skin a thick matting of collagen fibers forms the "corium" that gives the skin its toughness and plasticity. This corium layer in the hide of animals becomes the substance of leather after tanning. It is no accident that the investigations of leather chemists have made significant contributions to gerontology.

Several gerontologists have concluded that the aging of collagen and elastin (connective tissue) may be a major cause of mammalian senescence. The two leading proponents of this view are Dr. Robert R. Kohn of the Institute of Pathology, Western Reserve University in Cleveland, Ohio, and Dr. Harry Sobel, the Chief of Aging Research at the Veteran's Administration Hospital in Sepulveda, California.

Dr. Kohn believes that alterations in connective tissue can explain almost all of the characteristics of human aging. He considers cross-linking the primary cause of adverse changes in connective tissue components. Dr. Kohn theorizes that the increasing rigidity of small blood vessels can cause hypertension and arteriosclerosis and that the increased quantity of cross-linked collagen hinders the diffusion of hormones, nutrients and antibodies through the tissues. Dr. Kohn describes his current animal experiments: [7]

> We have some methods for testing the collagen theory of aging, as well as possibly lengthening the life-span. It should be possible to keep animals on a diet deficient in ascorbic acid so that maturation of collagen is slowed, but not deficient enough to produce symptoms of scurvy. Such animals should have a lengthened life-span. Also, the lathyrogen B-amino-propionitrile ... can be given to animals from the time of weaning in doses sufficient to slow down collagen cross linking but not enough to cause overt lathyrism.

Dr. Sobel's explanation of aging is essentially the same as that of Dr. Kohn. Dr. Sobel observes: [8]

> We have postulated that an increase in fibrillar density of the connective tissue would result in impaired delivery of oxygen and nutrients to the cells and removal of waste products from

the cells. . . . Other changes taking place in the ground substance may also influence diffusion. . . . Ground substance generally decreases as protein is lost from the body.

If the above theory is correct, we would expect the following changes to occur progressively as age advances: 1) increased susceptibility to systemic or local events which interfere with oxygen transport; 2) impaired rate of entry into and removal of substances from the blood stream; 3) adaptive phenomena, particularly in regard to hypoxia (lack of oxygen).

Dr. Sobel's analysis may also provide us with some understanding of the cause of cancer. Since the incidence of malignancies increases with age, many scientists have speculated about the possible relationship between malignancy and senescence.

As collagen around the cells becomes increasingly crosslinked, oxygen transport into the cells is impaired. All cells have an emergency survival mechanism called anaerobic metabolism whereby they use carbon dioxide rather than oxygen in metabolic processes. Dr. Sobel suggests that age changes in connective tissues eventually cause some cells to switch over to anaerobic metabolism as an adaptive measure for cellular survival: [9]

The need for adaptive adjustment to hypoxia (lack of oxygen) for survival of cells may result in another sequence of major impact. Consideration of the origins of neoplastic cells suggests that some arise from cells which were excessively stimulated, or inadequately nourished and oxygenated. The ensuing cellular mutations represent an irreversible adaptive change permitting these cells to survive in an environment which would otherwise be lethal.

The classical investigations of Warburg (1956) led him to the conclusion that the origin of cancer requires *irreversible* respiratory damage, but also increased glycolysis sufficient to compensate for the loss of the energy of respiration. This point of view suggests the development of an adaptive mechanism that permits survival under a degree of hypoxia which would otherwise be lethal. Goldblatt and Cameron (1953) were the first to produce cancer cells by growing cardiac fibroblasts with intermediate oxygen deficiency for years. They finally obtained transplantable cancer cells.

The revolutionary implications of Dr. Sobel's analysis are that the changes in connective tissues that occur with age may be a basic cause of cardiovascular disease (strokes and heart attacks). Cross-linking of collagen may create the morbid environmental conditions that cause normal cells to become malignant. The cross-linkage theory could prove to be the central foundation of a complete understanding of the biological processes that cause the major diseases.

Dr. Sobel has proposed therapeutic measures to compensate for the adverse changes caused by progressive collagen cross-linkages: [10]

> The rate of aging could be delayed by reducing collagen deposition or, in its presence, by allowing adequate quantities of oxygen and nutrients to reach the cells . . . it may be that increased gradients of oxygen, amino acids, glucose, and other nutrients, as well as hormones such as insulin, may be required in order to maintain the cells as they were at an earlier time.

Dr. Sobel points out that decreased intracellular growth hormone and insulin, both of which play a vital role in new protein synthesis, may be particularly significant. When these two hormones can be inexpensively synthesized, they will probably be of great importance in anti-aging hormone replacement therapy.

Dr. Sobel's solution to the hypoxia (lack of oxygen) problem is periodic sessions in hyperbaric chambers. These large-volume, high-pressure oxygen chambers enable large amounts of oxygen to be dissolved in the blood plasma. At three atmospheres (45 psi) there is enough dissolved oxygen to meet all body needs without using the red blood cells. At higher pressures the plasma can hold even more dissolved oxygen. Hyperbaric oxygen therapy has already cured gas gangrene and tetanus and promises to be of very great value in treating patients suffering from shock, accident injuries, hemorrhages, heart attacks and strokes.

There has been some speculation that dimethyl sulfoxide (DMSO) might serve as a "carrier," enabling hormones and oxygen to pass more readily through cross-linked collagen. Animal experiments with DMSO, though inconclusive, have not indicated that it will act in that capacity. Perhaps a fluorinated or deuterized molecular variant of DMSO (see Chapter 6) would produce the desired results.

The role of collagen in aging may have been overemphasized because collagen is so much easier to work with than most other proteins. There are, however, many unresolved questions. Highly cross-linked material isolated from aged human hearts does not appear to be derived from collagen. Also, Dr. Kohn's extensive experiments with the lathyrogen B-amino-propionitrile failed to extend the life-span of rats. Dr. Kohn observes: "The major problem with this type of experiment is, while an agent may inhibit the maturation or cross-linking of perhaps 20 percent of the collagen, the animal may compensate by simply synthesizing more collagen. Other problems are toxic side effects when agents are used in high concentrations."

Dr. Kohn has experiments under way investigating the influence of penicillamine, mercaptoethyl amine and butylated hydroxytoluene on the properties of connective tissue.

Scientists already know of a number of chemicals that seem to prevent cross-linking in newly formed collagen fibers. What is needed are the enzymes that will break down older cross-linked collagen and elastin so that the connective tissue can be restored to a more youthful state. The discovery of such enzymes is essential for progress in experimental gerontology. Even if the Bjorksten cross-linking aging theory is only applicable to connective tissue, it will enable man to control at least this cause of senescence.

8

~~~~~~~~~~~~~~~~~~~~~~~~~~~~~~~~~~~~

DNA and Somatic Mutations

THE cross-linkage theory of senescence falls within the first of Alex Comfort's three categories defined in Chapter 5—"that vigour declines as a result of changes in the properties of cells which are continually dividing."

The next theory which we will consider, the somatic mutation theory, is in the second main category of the probable causes of aging:

> Vigour declines through loss of, or injury to, the non-multiplying postmitotic cells; in other words, irreplaceable cells are lost with time.

The somatic mutation theory states that somatic mutations are the fundamental cause of cell injury and result in the malfunction or death of irreplaceable cells in the brain and other vital organs. Somatic cells are those responsible for the maintenance of the organism, in contrast to the germ cells which control reproduction of the species. Most of the cells in a mammal are somatic cells.

The development of the somatic mutation theory was made possible by the revolutionary discoveries in molecular biology which enabled scientists to decipher many fundamental life processes, and by the growing interest in radiation biology.

We now know that the vital ingredient in all living things is a giant spiraling molecule of nucleic acid called DNA (deoxyribonucleic acid). DNA molecules are visualized as a combination of two long, interweaving chains, a double helix. When the two long chains are pulled apart, each half contains all that is necessary to re-create the missing half, and become a complete DNA molecule. This regeneration is the basic process of life. When scientists and biologists decipher the molecular code hidden in the complex, submicroscopic world of DNA biochemistry, they will know the exact way genetic patterns are transmitted.

The function of both germ cells and somatic cells is determined by thousands of different DNA molecules. These DNA molecules are found in chromosomes, complex combinations of DNA and various protein molecules (the cells in man have 46 chromosomes). The DNA molecules in the chromosomes create several different kinds of RNA (ribonucleic acid), a giant, spiraling molecule similar in structure to DNA. By a process still not completely understood, the various forms of RNA are able to produce all the substances which make up the tissues of the body.

The DNA in human chromosomes contains the code for over 100,000 different kinds of protein which are produced by the RNA molecules. These include all the structural protein, hormones and enzymes. In the somatic cells, enzymes are the most numerous and vital of the protein molecules produced by the DNA-RNA process. Enzymes are essential catalytic agents in all biological processes. They break down food protein into free amino acids available for cell growth. Other enzymes are active in the synthesis of protein. Each DNA molecule is attended by its own special enzymes which aid the molecule in repairing itself, reproducing itself, and in synthesizing RNA. Some enzymes join molecules together. The enzymes which break large molecules apart (mentioned in

Chapter 6), including molecules of cross-linked protein and DNA, may be the key to an effective anti-aging therapy.

The somatic mutation theory has been effectively summarized by Dr. Howard J. Custis, the chairman of the Biology Department at the Brookhaven National Laboratory in Upton, New York: [1]

> The genetic information in the somatic cells, as contained in the DNA molecules, controls the function of the individual cell. Indeed from what we now know it appears that the only way in which a permanent change, short of death, can be effected in the cell is by a change in the DNA or chromosome structure. All other damage can be repaired. A change in the DNA of a cell is referred to as a mutation, whether the cell is a somatic or a germ cell and whether or not it ever undergoes division again. If a somatic cell undergoes mutation, it is a different cell designed to perform a different function. However, if a change occurs in a somatic cell of a character not necessary for the function of that cell, then the consequences will be unimportant. For example, if the gene for eye color is mutated in a liver cell, nothing of consequence will result. But if the gene controlling the synthesis of an essential enzyme is altered, the cell will no longer perform its function well.

In other words, a somatic mutation is some form of alteration in a DNA molecule that causes it to produce faulty RNA, which in turn can no longer synthesize the hormone, enzyme, or protein that is the end product of cell activity. A somatic mutation might also include damage that would prevent DNA from producing any RNA at all.

In the dividing cells it is assumed that mutated cells will be at a selective disadvantage from their normal counterparts. The struggle for existence in constantly dividing tissue would cause the mutated cells to be eliminated. Therefore, constantly dividing cells remain young, even in an old animal. It can be assumed that animals that do not stop growing, such as the giant tortoise, may not age because all their cells continue to divide as long as they live.

In adult mammals, the important cells in the brain and other vital organs do not continue to divide. A somatic mutation in such a cell would probably cause it to malfunction. Mutations in vital DNA molecules would prevent essential functions, in some cases killing a cell that is not replaceable. It is estimated that the adult human loses 10,000 brain neurons every day.

Alex Comfort attributes the popularity of the somatic mutation theory to the fact that "mutative changes in cell lines would probably lead to eventual aging if no other cause did so first." The readiness with which the somatic mutation theory lends itself to elaborate mathematical models has made it attractive to many physicists and mathematicians, though the theory is still surrounded by controversy. Many gerontologists doubt that mutation-caused cell loss is high enough to be responsible for aging.

Dr. J. Maynard Smith of the University of Sussex in England expresses this present uncertainty: [2]

> Even if no other senescent changes occurred, animals, some of whose essential tissues consist of nondividing cells, would ultimately die from the effects of somatic mutations. The question at issue is not whether somatic mutations occur, but whether they are common enough to contribute significantly to aging.

Dr. Robert R. Kohn observes: [3]

> The role of cellular aging should be considered against a background of two concepts. First, aging of a higher animal is a generalized process occurring throughout the body. . . . Second, the reserve of cells in various organs is enormous. It is well known that a human being can survive without symptoms with less than 40% of his liver, part of one kidney, one lung, fractions of stomach and intestine, etc. Thus, if aging of the intact animal results from aging of its cells, we would expect to find cell death or loss of cellular function in organs throughout the aging body, and we would expect the loss of very large numbers of cells—perhaps 50% or more of those present in the young adult.

A review of the history of the somatic mutation theory will help clarify these different points of view.

Ionizing Radiation and Mutations

During World War II scientists discovered that animals subjected to ionizing radiation appeared to age rapidly and have a shorter life expectancy than controls who were not subject to radiation. Radiation is a well-known carcinogenic agent, and part of the life shortening was the result of an increased incidence of cancer. However, irradiated animals that did not develop malignancies also had shorter life-spans. The conclusion was that the degenerative diseases associated with senescence are accelerated by radiation, and some are accelerated more than others. Since the pattern of fatal diseases in irradiated and control animals was not identical, the action of radiation is not a simple increase in the normal rate of senescence.

The actual mechanisms by which radiation shortens life are still a subject of scientific debate. Johan Bjorksten points out that ionizing radiation produces hydrogen peroxide and free radicals (powerful cross-linking agents) throughout the body. Dr. Robert R. Kohn observes that "one of the very conspicuous and consistent changes after x-irradiation is not what would be interpreted as mutation but as a fibrosis around the capillaries," or increased formation of collagen in the connective tissues. Dr. J. Maynard Smith suggests that "the life-shortening effects of X-rays and some chemical mutagens arise because they break chromosomes, particularly in dividing tissues, and not because they cause point mutations." Radiation damage to RNA molecules may be more important than the damage to DNA molecules.

Most radiation biologists attribute radiation life-shortening to alterations in chromosome DNA (somatic mutations). We know that radiation produces mutations in the germ cells. Defective DNA in ova and sperm can cause horrible defects in succeeding generations. The uncertainty and fear about genetic mutations provided much of the early stimulus to radiation biology. It is not surprising, therefore, that radiation biologists thought in terms of DNA alteration when presented with the two most important questions in biology: Why do mammals age? What can be done to prevent aging?

Dr. Leo Szilard (1898–1964), a leading nuclear physicist, was one of several brilliant scientists who attempted to evolve a detailed theory of radiation and aging. In 1959, Dr. Szilard presented an elaborate somatic mutation theory which stated that the primary step in aging is a "hit" on one chromosome of a somatic cell which renders all of the chromosome's genes inactive. Szilard also assumed that man is born with a number of genetic faults (a mutation in one of the genes essential to the proper functioning of a somatic cell). Szilard refined his hit-fault hypothesis into a complex mathematical model which seemed to fit the pattern of mammalian aging. Seasoned gerontologists quickly pointed out, however, that the theory did not conform to the life-span patterns of inbred and hybrid animals. Alex Comfort commented that Szilard's theory was "mathematically ingenious but biologically implausible."

Dr. Szilard modified his theory somewhat and was disturbed when new objections were raised. His outspoken and candid attitude offended some gerontologists. During one meeting he said: "I have the only theory of aging, all other explanations are simply guesses."

The cross-linking theory is consistent with Szilard's data that aging is essentially a random process. Dr. Szilard expressed great interest in cross-linking phenomena, and wanted to meet with Johan Bjorksten. Szilard's untimely death intervened. Had he lived, he probably would have broadened his theory to include the cross-linking of vital DNA and protein.

Dr. Howard J. Curtis, leading exponent of the somatic mutation theory, has attempted to provide experimental evidence to overcome the basic objections to the theory. He admits that "there is no known method of measuring mutations in individual somatic cells." Mutations in reproductive cells can only be determined by the number of defects in the off-spring. The mutation rate in somatic cells would have to be 10 to 20 times greater than the mutation rate in reproductive cells if somatic mutations are the primary cause of senescence.

Dr. Curtis has conducted a number of experiments producing chromosome abnormalities in the dividing liver cells of mice. He contends that these experiments demonstrate that somatic cells do have a much higher mutation rate than reproductive cells, though other scientists have offered different explanation for liver chromosome abnormalities. Dr. Curtis proposes to extend the life-span by modifying the basic cause of somatic mutations.

In summary, the present evidence for and against the somatic mutation theory suggests that it is a highly plausible explanation of senescence, but like the cross-linking theory, can only be completely proved by refining anti-aging therapies that would prevent or correct somatic mutation damage to DNA molecules in the chromosomes.

Possible Causes and Corrections of Somatic Mutations

We are all subject to "background" radiation throughout our lives. This radiation comes from many sources, including cosmic rays and naturally radioactive elements in the soil. The human body contains several radioactive elements, carbon-14 and potassium-40 for example. It is estimated that the total lifetime dosage of background radiation is about 20 roentgen (R). It requires a single radiation exposure of 400 R to kill a human.

Dr. G. Failla has suggested that background radiation received during embryonic development, when the radiation sensitivity of mammalian cells is considerably higher than it is after birth, accelerates aging in later development. The only way to prove or disprove Dr. Failla's suggestion would be to raise a colony of radiation-free animals (see Chapter 14, page 202), an experiment involving a corrective therapy. It is, however, extremely doubtful that radiation received before birth would have a "time-bomb" aging reaction during the later stages of adult evolution. Almost all gerontologists now agree that background radiation is not a significant cause of mammalian aging.

Dr. Curtis has analyzed other possible causes of accelerated somatic mutations. He observes that the cells of some insects and plants contain a *mutator gene*. When a given amount of time has elapsed or certain environmental conditions are present, the mutator genes cause a mutagenic compound to be synthesized within the cell (through a DNA-RNA process). These mutagenic compounds act as catalysts, increasing the number of somatic mutations in cell chromosome DNA. The increased mutation rate quickly produces a large number of defective cells, finally killing the insect or plant. There is, however, no experimental evidence that mutator genes exist in mammalian cells.

The search for mammalian mutator genes requires the most imaginative of experimental procedures in molecular biology. Though mutator genes are probably not there, the ancillary discoveries made in their quest would fully justify a significant research effort.

If experiments demonstrate that mutator genes do, in fact, exist in mammals, subsequent research should elucidate their operating mechanisms. Once we know how they function, it should be possible to develop an anti-aging therapy that would counteract the effect of mutator genes.

Dr. Curtis also mentions the possible existence of a *death hormone,* a mutagenic hormone secreted by an endocrine gland that directly or indirectly increases the somatic mutation rate. But a death hormone is less probable than mammalian mutator genes, though if it exists, it would be easier to locate and isolate. The search for a death hormone might uncover other hormones which play a beneficial role in life processes. The biological rationale behind the hypothetical mutator gene and death hormone is based on natural selection. Some scientists suggest that aging may actually be beneficial to the survival of the species. This is a complex, speculative argument, however, with no scientific facts to support it. It might be properly placed in the "after three martinis" category of intellectual reasoning, although if senescence has evolved through natural selection, a death hormone or mutator gene might be the timing mechanism.

However, few animals actually reach the senescence stage in nature. Disease or predators usually kill them before they exhibit any significant signs of aging.

The DNA Repair Process

Some years ago scientists discovered that if animals were exposed to X-rays or gamma rays very slowly, over a long period of time, a given dose would be only about one-quarter as effective as the same dose given within a few hours. For example, 2,000 rads of gamma rays given to mice at a slow dose rate over several months will produce about the same effect as a single dose of 500 rads. The measured effects include the degree of life shortening, and the chromosome aberrations observed in dividing cells and genetic mutations in the baby mice conceived after the radiation exposure. Though we cannot measure somatic mutations, these observed changes provide strong evidence that somatic mutations would follow the same patterns.

In 1960 Dr. Ruth Hill of Columbia University discovered that DNA in mammalian cells has self-repair enzymes. Each portion of a DNA strand has the same or comparable molecular code as the portion of the strand opposite to it. Low-level X-rays and gamma rays most frequently damage only one side of the two interwound DNA strands. The self-repair enzymes travel along the DNA molecule, remove damaged sections and grow new replicas identical to the undamaged opposite portion of the DNA molecule.

The actual mechanism by which these enzymes repair damaged DNA is not fully understood. Two explanations have been proposed which are compatible with the experimental data. One is called "cut and patch" and the other is referred to as "patch and cut." The differences are highly technical, and present research should soon determine which one is correct. From a standpoint of mutation repair, the end result is the same.

Not all forms of radiation have the same effect on chromosome DNA in mammalian cells. Neutron irradiation, for example, depends only on the dose, and is independent of the dose rate. It is assumed that neutron irradiation creates dense local ionization around various portions of DNA molecules. The free radicals and other reactive chemicals produced by such strong local ionization cause chromosome DNA damage too severe to be easily repaired. Perhaps both sides of the interwound DNA strands are damaged at the same time, or the enzyme repair process is in some way hindered.

When the animals are irradiated slowly over a long period of time, the DNA repair enzymes can correct most of the X-ray and gamma-ray damage. An acute dose administered quickly is four times more damaging because the repair process is simply overwhelmed. It works slowly and cannot speed up to match a saturation radiation dose.

The DNA enzyme repair process appears to be controlled by four genes. If any one of the four is crippled, the process stops. Should somatic mutations be found to be a major cause of aging, then these genes would assume vital importance. Closely related species of animals have markedly different average life-spans. Perhaps genetic variations in their DNA repair genes explain these discrepancies.

There is a great deal still to be learned about the DNA repair process, with many questions yet to be answered. If the repair enzymes are deficient, could they be supplied by injection? The repair system is probably a metabolic process that cannot function in the absence of oxygen. Would this system be more effective in a moderate-pressure hyperbaric chamber, which would supply cells with additional oxygen dissolved in the blood plasma? Increased cross-linked collagen in the connective tissues probably reduces the amount of oxygen that reaches the chromosomes. Is this slow reduction of intracellular oxygen the timing mechanism that shuts off the DNA repair process, and allows the increase in permanent somatic mutations that contribute to senescence? If the old cross-linked collagen in the connective tissues around the cells could be broken up, would the increased oxygen, hormones and nutrients reactivate the intracellular DNA repair process? Perhaps this would save many fixed cells that die with increasing frequency as the body ages.

Dr. Curtis is optimistic about the prospect for an anti-aging therapy to counteract somatic mutations. He believes that accelerated research will enable scientists to refine methods that will both prevent and repair damage to DNA molecules. He points out that it is now possible to favorably alter chromosome stability in plants, and "as we learn more about the forces and factors stabilizing large molecules it should be possible to do this for animals. . . . Progress in the field will require a much more thorough knowledge of the structure of large molecules and the forces which stabilize them." [4]

Dr. Curtis stresses the potential of molecular biology in respect to the somatic mutation theory of aging: [5]

> If it is possible to alter the chromosome stability of plant cells, it should also be possible to do so for mammalian cells. Likewise, since it is possible to either counteract or augment various enzymatic processes which occur in mammalian cells, it should be possible eventually to augment the enzymatic processes in these cells responsible for chromosomal repair. And finally, it

should eventually be possible to determine and control the genes within the mammalian cells which may be responsible for at least part of the molecular instability of these cells.

These are difficult assignments and will not be accomplished tomorrow. But I am convinced that if the maximum human life span is to be appreciably extended, it will be necessary to solve them, and I believe them to be soluble.

The Artificial Virus and Genetic Modification

There is another conceptual approach to repairing damaged DNA that is now in scientific vogue involving viruses. A virus consists of a DNA or RNA molecule covered by a jacket of protein. The protein coat enables the viral DNA or RNA to be injected through the walls of body cells. Once inside, the viral DNA or RNA uses the cell machinery to reproduce itself, often killing the cell and releasing the multiplied viruses.

In some cases, when viral DNA enters a cell, it attaches itself to one of the chromosomes and actually becomes part of the cell's genetic machinery. Sometimes this new chromosomal DNA radically alters the function of the entire cell. The virus theory of cancer is based on the assumption that an invading viral DNA molecule will attach itself to a chromosome and cause the cell to begin a pattern of rapid, uncontrolled malignant growth.

If viral DNA can cause damage, it should be theoretically possible to create new viral DNA that would be beneficial. There are more than 40 hereditary genetic diseases caused by faulty genes. Scientists are now attempting to find means of producing the DNA molecule that would correct the genetic fault creating the disease. Once the correct DNA molecule can be produced in quantity, it must be given a protein jacket that would penetrate only the cells in which the operation of the defective gene is important. These artificial viruses would then be injected into the body, and travel to their intracellular targets, where they would correct a hereditary chromosomal defect.

It has been suggested that artificial viruses might be created that would repair somatic mutation damage in aging cells. Perhaps the genes responsible for producing DNA repair enzymes could be replaced by artificial viruses. Since all the body's somatic cells contain the same set of chromosomes, this is not an unreasonable possibility.

Genetic modification through artificial viruses could improve vitality, virility and intelligence. Permanent memory seems to be stored in RNA molecules produced by chromosomal DNA in the brain neurons. Perhaps artificial viruses could make all 10 billion brain neurons more effective. Other artificial viruses may supply added strength. Perhaps even the answer to the perennial search for sexual rejuvenation will be found in artificial viruses.

The artificial virus could make possible significant genetic modifications in the adult. Skin color or hair, for example, might be permanently changed. Perhaps we can create a superior race via the hypodermic syringe, rather than rely on a slow process of eugenic breeding.

However, the artificial-virus approach to aging and other problems faces several biological barriers, the most important being the body's immunologic system. It would be necessary to block or immobilize the immunologic system temporarily to prevent it from producing antibodies that would kill the artificial viruses before they reached their destinations.

The possibility of an artificial virus opens up a means of permanently altering the immunological system itself. This may be the key to preventing immunologic rejection of human organ transplants. Artificial viruses might even modify the immunologic system so that animal tissue would not be rejected in man, thereby making available an unlimited supply of replacement organs.

The mass production of artificial viruses should not be difficult. One can imagine a complete factory containing thousands of automatically controlled human tissue cell cultures, each one at the right temperature, receiving an optimum mixture of hormones and nutrients. The separate tissue cultures would each produce large numbers of a specific artificial virus which would be removed for subsequent human genetic modification.

The artificial virus would also make it possible to replace faulty or missing RNA within somatic cells. This replacement would supply an RNA core for our artificial virus. Artificial RNA viruses should be particularly suitable as anti-aging therapy agents.

Of course, applicable research is only in the very early stages. However, it has been proved that DNA in natural viruses can become a permanent part of chromosomal DNA in human cells. Estimates of how long it will take scientists to create artificial viruses range from 5 to 50 years. The accelerating pace of scientific achievement suggests that the optimists will be right. It would seem possible that genetic engineering with artificial viruses will be refined within 10 to 20 years.

Within this century scientists are likely to unravel the fundamental chemistry of heredity. At the very least we should be able to alter the physical and mental characteristics of succeeding generations. We could create a race with the most desirable characteristics and eliminate harmful genes which cause inherited handicaps. The key to heredity may also provide the formula that will eventually enable man to control biological aging.

Cross-Linking and Somatic Mutations

Howard J. Curtis confirms that "the cause of spontaneous mutations is still not known." Experimental evidence suggests that somatic mutations may be partly or wholly caused by cross-linking. There have been a number of attempts to increase the somatic mutation rate in animals by giving them near-fatal doses of chemical mutagens, such as nitrogen mustard. But these chemical mutagens did not reduce the average life-span of the test animals. Alex Comfort has some particularly important comments on these experiments: [6]

> In any case we have been speaking loosely of mutation when what we really mean is a change in the cell's information and control mechanism. Other factors and processes that point to chromosome change are almost certainly at work; thus of the chemicals which can cause mutation, only those which are active cross-linking agents appear to shorten life on the same scale as radiation.

In 1953 Dr. Francis H. C. Crick, Dr. James D. Watson, and Dr. Maurice H. F. Wilkins deciphered the molecular structure of the DNA molecule (they later received the Nobel Prize for their discovery). At that time Johan Bjorksten brought out the possibility that both genetic and somatic mutations are caused by cross-linkage between DNA molecules or between a DNA molecule and a free protein molecule within the cell. Nine years later, in 1962, Frederic Verzár independently suggested that "DNA might be impaired by a gradual cross-linking of its hydrogen bonds." Dr. Verzár also observed: [7]

> If DNA also ages by accumulated cross linking between the helices, this would probably inhibit its ability to pass on "information," and resulting in a decrease of anabolic processes such as protein synthesis and enzyme production, which must of course reduce the activities of the cell in general.
>
> Thus aging of DNA may be the factor which leads to the aging of all those cells which do not undergo mitosis (division), and this includes the cells of the central nervous system, the ovum cells of the ovary, and the cells of any other organs if once their mitotic activity (cell division) comes to a standstill.

Dr. Bjorksten pointed out that other scientists have demonstrated that cross-linking mutagenetic compounds are up to 50 times more active in the production of chromosome breaks than mutagens which are not cross-linking chemicals. He also observes that ionizing radiation produces free radicals which are powerful cross-linkers. Bjorksten explains the differences between irradiation biological damage and natural aging as due to the fact that radiation also causes some nuclear chain fission (the splitting of the atom nucleus). Fission reactions have biological effects that are quite different from cross-linking.

Dr. Bjorksten believes that "somatic mutations are cellular phenomena, which are consequences of cross-linkages which prevent the genetically significant DNA molecules from parting after a division, or which tie together template and product." In other words, the somatic mutation theory may actually be part of the cross-linking explanation of senescence. Dr. Bjorksten concludes that "cross-linking is the only known process by which extremely small quantities of any one of many known metabolites at the wrong place and time can and indeed do impair or destroy the function of two giant molecules. . . . We do not question Curtis' conclusion that chromosome damage occurs in nondividing cells on aging, since cross-linking has been shown to occur both with nucleic acids and proteins." [8]

The greatest weakness of the somatic mutation theory as presented by Howard J. Curtis is that it does not explain the biological mechanism behind Dr. McCay's remarkable achievement in extending the life-span of underfed rats. Dr. Curtis comments: "It would seem wiser at the present time to admit that we do not know why these animals live longer, and reserve judgment until more is known about them." [9]

If one assumes that the majority of somatic mutations are caused by cross-linking, then the somatic mutation theory can be used to explain the results of the McCay underfeeding experiments. The small amounts of food were quickly metabolized to harmless end products of water and carbon dioxide. There were very few intermediate metabolic compounds which could have caused cross-linking in chromosomal

DNA. The fact that the cross-linking explanation of somatic mutations can explain Dr. McCay's results provides additional support for Dr. Bjorksten's comprehensive elucidation of mammalian senescence.

Dr. Peter Alexander at the Chester Beatty Cancer Research Institute in London showed that cross-linking mutagens greatly reduced the life-span of mice. He found that mutagens which do not also cause cross-linking did not greatly reduce their life-span. Mutagens are chemicals which are known to cause genetic mutations and are assumed to cause somatic mutations. Dr. Alexander's research provides evidence for the contention that somatic mutations are a less important cause of aging than cross-linkage.

The cross-linking theory and the somatic mutations theory are the two most plausible explanations of aging. The cross-linking theory explains aging as a result of both intra- and extracellular activity. The somatic mutation theory explains aging as a consequence of intracellular change. The leading proponents of these theories, Johan Bjorksten and Howard J. Curtis, have outlined research options that promise effective anti-aging therapies. These programs are of utmost importance and should be allotted adequate funds, personnel, and resources.

Dr. Curtis recognizes that aging has more than one cause: "A mammal is an extremely complex structure and can and does go bad in a wide variety of ways. Thus, the only real problem is that percentage of the total aging picture is caused by the various phenomena which one can point to. I, personally, believe that somatic mutations plays a very dominant role in the process, but there are many secondary roles which are necessary for the development of the total syndrome." [10]

Somatic mutations are important even if future research indicates that they are not the major cause of aging. For instance, it may be found that cross-linking (including cross-linked DNA), is responsible for 80 percent of aging, and somatic mutations caused by factors other than cross-linking are responsible for the remaining 20 percent of senescence. If all cross-linkage damage were prevented and corrected, it would still be vitally important to correct the remaining cause of biological deterioration.

It is too early to evaluate whether some of the bolder proposals of the molecular biologists will play an important role in controlling the aging process. The possibility of correcting faulty or age-damaged DNA with artificial viruses is certainly the most exotic possible addition to a comprehensive anti-aging therapy.

It is interesting to note that leading molecular biologists are much more optimistic concerning our chances to control the aging process than are many leading gerontologists. Cal Tech's Dr. James Bonner predicts that "the capability to live 200 years will soon be within our grasp." Dr. Robert L. Sinsheimer, also of Cal Tech, predicts that advances in biology will soon give man "the power to live indefinitely." Molecular biology is generously funded while gerontologists receive limited financial support. Perhaps the degree of optimism expressed by scientists in any field is directly related to the financial resources available for research.

The dim outlines of the relationships between cross-linking, somatic mutations, and possible modifications in DNA are now emerging. Our new understanding of fundamental life processes at the molecular level has enabled imaginative scientists to explore exciting conceptual approaches for the control of all biological phenomena, including senescence. With adequate support some—perhaps all—of these possibilities will be realized before the end of the twentieth century.

9

^^^^^^^^^^^^^^^^^^^^^^^^^^^^^^^^^^^

The Immunologic Theory

THE basic somatic mutation theory explains aging as a consequence of intracellular reactions. The mutations are assumed to impair cellular functions. In 1959, the Australian Nobel Laureate Sir Macfarlane Burnet proposed a modification of the somatic mutation theory in which aging was thought to be a result of reactions between cells rather than reactions within cells. Burnet suggested that the immunologic system which protects the body from disease may also be the cause of senescence.

The immunologic system produces antibodies which destroy invading microorganisms. The introduction of any foreign protein into the body, such as a transplanted kidney, will stimulate the immunologic system into producing defensive antibodies. Antibodies are believed to be produced by lymphocyte cells which transmit this acquired defensive power to their progeny when they divide. Normally a youthful immunologic system recognizes the body's original tissues and does not produce antibodies that attack its own protein.

Sir Macfarlane Burnet has suggested, though not proved, that somatic mutations in the lymphocyte cells cause them to produce antibodies against the body's own tissue. Such mutations in the lymphocytes would be a random phenomena, with the percentage of defective lymphocytes gradually increasing. The cells of the body would be subject to a constant attack of increasing severity by its own antibodies.

The American gerontologist most active in immunologic aging research, UCLA's Dr. Roy L. Walford, has proposed that somatic mutations in cells throughout the body activate the immunologic system against these altered cells. Since the mutated cells are not too dissimilar from their normal neighbors, the same antibodies might also attack the normal cells. Dr. Walford is presently writing a monograph on the immunologic theory of aging.

It is possible that aging can be explained by both immunologic theories. Mutated lymphocytes may produce destructive antibodies, and mutated cells might also stimulate the production of antibodies that attack normal body tissue.

Autoimmunity has been definitely implicated in a number of diseases common in old age, including arthritis, diabetes, myasthenia, multiple sclerosis and thyroiditis. Some forms of cancer are thought to be related to autoimmunity, and malignancy is generally believed to be the result of mutation caused by radiation, viruses and other changes not yet thoroughly understood.

Fortunately, the immunologic theories of aging are more easily subject to proof-of-principle experiments than most other aging theories.

Immunologic Aging Experiments

Dr. Walford has conducted a number of experiments to show that immunologic phenomena do cause changes resembling natural aging. In one series of experiments he created parabiotic Syrian hamsters. The genetic differences between the tissues of the joined hamsters were expected to cause a slow low-grade immunologic battle between the parabiot partners. If aging is primarily an immunologic phenomena, he reasoned, then parabiosis should accelerate the entire process of senescence.

The hamster parabiots appeared to age prematurely and tended to die of diseases characteristic of older hamsters. Experiments with rat parabiots produced similar results. On the other hand, long-term parabiotic mice exhibited no change in the rate of aging or disease patterns.

In another experiment Dr. Walford injected newborn mice with lymphoid cells from mice with a slightly different immunogenic nature. The average life-span of these recipient mice was considerably shortened by fatal malignant diseases which appeared at an earlier age than in the control animals.

Parabiosis and the injection of foreign lymphoid cells are somewhat radical biological procedures. They might cause life shortening for reasons unrelated to the basic causes of mammalian aging. Experiments that would prolong the life-span by altering the immunologic system would be far more convincing than life-span reduction experiments. Again we come to the fact that a theory of aging can only be completely proved by extending the mammalian life-span using corrective therapies based on the theory.

The effort in recent years to do successful organ transplants by suppressing the body's immunologic system provides a great deal of pertinent information for immunologic aging research. There have been over 1,000 successful kidney transplants between persons that are not identical twins. In most organ transplants, drugs are used to suppress the body's immunologic system. A very delicate balance is required. Too much suppression will render the immunologic system ineffective in protecting the body against microorganisms so that a relatively minor bacterial infection could cause death. If the immunologic system is not sufficiently depressed, it produces antibodies that cause the transplanted organ to be rejected. The greater the genetic difference between the transplant organ and the recipient, the greater the immunologic reaction.

A number of different drugs have been used to prevent the rejection of transplanted organs. Other drugs have produced beneficial results in the treatment of autoimmune diseases. If self-destructive immunologic mechanisms are a major cause of aging, then one or more of these drugs should be useful in extending the life-spans of experimental animals.

Dr. Walford gave mice the immunosuppressive drug Imuran on a daily basis beginning in late adulthood. The mice given the drug had a median survival time of 103 weeks compared to a median survival time for control mice of 94 weeks. Dr. Walford is continuing variations of this experiment with different drug levels of Imuran.

The Imuran results to date have produced a life extension of about 10 percent. While this is not a dramatic increase, it should be remembered that these drug experiments are just beginning and preliminary results can be misleading. If a number of experiments using different immunosuppressive drugs, drug dosages and combinations of drugs all produce life-span extensions of about 10 percent, then one might conclude that immunologic explanations account for only a small fraction of senescence.

There have been other experiments whose findings indirectly support immunologic aging theories. Transplants between highly inbred mice will usually "take" without any immunologic reaction in the same way as transplants between identical twins. In one series of experiments it was found that 75 percent of skin grafts between very young inbred mice were accepted. The number of successful skin grafts decreased as the mice aged until no grafts were successful when old mice were used as both donors and recipients. These experimental results can be explained as "immunologic diversification." That is, as the animals grew older, they may have developed more and more minor immunologic differences as a result of somatic mutations which made it increasingly difficult to effect a successful skin transplant.

The mice skin graft experiments could serve as a model for a unique human experiment. Skin transplants could be made between identical twins of different ages. Such transplants would be harmless and would require only a minor surgical procedure. Of greater interest would be the transplant results between identical twins of advanced years. Skin graft rejection of transplants between older twins would provide strong evidence in support of immunologic diversification.

There are other phenomena which support the immunologic theory. The amount of gamma globulin, that portion of blood plasma that carries antibodies, increases with age. The spleen, important in antibody production, also increases in relative body weight in most mammals as they age. Roy L. Walford explains McCay's experiments as a suppression of the immunologic system: [1]

> Severe underfeeding during the first third or half of the rat's life greatly increases its ultimate longevity. Now, in starved rats, the spleen, gastrointestinal tract, and liver show the greatest weight loss of all organs. These organs are rich in immunological tissue. It has also been noted that malnutrition leads to profound involution of the thymus, which is according to recent knowledge the master lymphoid organ. These results suggest that the McCay experiment can be interpreted as immunologic suppression, or as slowing-up of immune development.

Dr. Walford has some interesting comments on radiation effects and drugs which cause mutations: [2]

> Irradiation is a mutagenic agent that should lead to immunogenetic diversification of the body's (lymphoid and other) cells. ... But irradiation also *suppresses* the immune response. Thus two opposing effects, one causing immunogenetic diversification and the other inhibiting the immunologic consequences of that diversification, can be envisaged. Some of the seemingly anomalous findings with regard to the effect of irradiation and radiomimetic drugs might be interpretable in terms of such opposing

effects. Nitrogen mustard is a radiomimetic drug, but it also powerfully depresses the immune response. It does not cause life shortening. Myleran and chlorambucil do shorten life-span and seem not to be effective as suppressors of immunity.

The incidence of autoimmune diseases increases with age. But, as Alex Comfort points out, they are "notoriously more prevalent in females than in males." Dr. Walford, however, divides autoimmune diseases into separate categories. He describes one category of autoimmune reactions as actual "diseases of aging" and says these are more common in males than in females.

There is no question that the incidence of autoimmune diseases increases with age, but then so does the incidence of other degenerative diseases. The observed patterns of auto-immune diseases among the elderly will not answer the crucial questions about immunologic aging theories. New experiments are needed that will show the effects on the life-span of various modifications of the immunologic system.

The most conclusive experiments would measure life-span changes brought about by the complete suppression of the immunologic system at a very early age. Such experiments are now possible using germ-free animals. In the absence of bacteria much higher dosages of immunosuppressive drugs can be used, since the "delicate balance" problem in administering such drugs is not important.

Germ-free animals can be used in irradiation experiments. Relatively high radiation levels shorten the life-span of animals, presumably because of an increased somatic mutation rate (which may cause immunologic aging). Radiation also suppresses the immunologic system. Do the two effects cancel each other? Would one predominate? Different levels of radiation given to germ-free animals over various time periods would help answer these questions.

In recent years a great deal has been learned about the role of the thymus gland in the early development of the immunologic system. There is considerable evidence that small lymphocyte cells travel from the thymus shortly after birth and seed the lympth nodes for further lymphocyte production of circulating plasma cells. It is the circulating plasma-cell lymphocytes that actually synthesize the antibodies.

The number of circulating lymphocytes may offer some clues to aging. In the short-lived mouse, lymphocytes constitute some 70 percent of all white blood cells. In the long-lived human they represent only 20 to 25 percent.

In one experiment, the development of the immunologic system in mice was retarded by removing the thymus gland within 24 hours of birth. These thymectomized mice grew normally for several weeks or months but soon died of a wasting disease characterized by loss of weight, weakness, lethargy and diarrhea. Autopsies indicate that these mice had a very low circulating lymphocyte level and suffered atrophy of the lymphoid tissue. Since the mice did not reject skin grafts from unrelated mice, it is obvious that the development of the immunologic system had been significantly retarded.

Germ-free mice thymectomized at birth did not develop this wasting syndrome. In fact, some were alive and reproducing 231 days after the operation. The immunologic system of thymectomized germ-free animals could be further suppressed with immunosuppressive drugs or radiation. Another experimental possibility is the creation of thymectomized hamster parabiots.

Germ-free animal experiments should be crucial in understanding the extent to which the immunologic process contributes to senescence. Unfortunately there are some problems with germ-free animals that must be solved first, the most serious being an increase in the size of the cecum, a blind pouch that opens into the upper part of the large intestine. In normal mice the cecum accounts for 1 to 3 percent of body weight. In germ-free mice the cecum may grow to as much as 20 to 25 percent of the animal's body weight. The large mass of the cecum frequently kills germ-free animals by rupturing or twisting, thereby releasing its poisonous fluids into the bloodstream. Solutions to problems which develop in the experimental use of germ-free animals are described in Chapter 14. The use of large germ-free animals, for example, makes possible anti-aging immunological suppression experiments that may be applicable to adult humans.

The circulating lymphocytes originally pass through an arterylike portion of the lymphatic system called the thoracic duct. In recent human organ transplantation experiments, surgeons sever the thoracic duct and attach it to a synthetic plastic tube which extends outside the body and is then passed back into the body to be joined to the other end of the severed thoracic duct. The portion of the tube extending outside the body is irradiated. The radiation suppresses antibody production in the circulating lymphocytes, allowing the transplanted organs to "take." Initial human experiments in organ transplantation indicate that this somewhat complex procedure is more effective than the use of immunosuppressive drugs.

If future research demonstrates that autoimmune reactions are a major cause of aging, the extended thoracic duct may be a favored means of reducing self-devouring antibodies in older humans. Such a surgical modification might also be used to introduce anti-aging hormones, enzymes and other chemicals into the body.

Cross-Linking and the Immunologic Theory

We have seen throughout this book that the major aging theories are often complementary. Dr. Walford suggests that "cross-linking might lead to somatic mutation and the latter could be expressed pathogenetically as immunogenic diversification with an accompanying auto-immunity." [3] Cross-linking, somatic mutations and autoimmune reactions are probably the three most plausible explanations of mammalian senescence. Dr. Walford's well-chosen words may even be the outline of a composite aging theory. He singles out Dr. Bjorksten's cross-linking theory as particularly relevant to the immunologic theory of senescence.[4]

> The cross-linking theory of aging can in fact explain quite a large body of gerontologic data ... antibodies may be ideal "cross-linking" agents. As few as 400–500 molecules of antibody globulin, i.e., quantitatively quite a small amount can hold two erythrocytes together. Furthermore, antigen-antibody precipitates are quite insoluble and could well form a "frozen metabolic pool." ... Insulin in diabetics with prior exposure to insulin was not readily degraded in vivo, suggesting interference of antibody with protein breakdown. ... It has been demonstrated that antibody to bovine serum albumin significantly shields the antigen from digestion by papin.

Dr. Walford mentions that very little is known about effects of immunological reactions on biochemical processes: "There is some evidence that proteins after combination with antibodies are rendered less susceptible to enzymic degradation. It is a well known fact of aging that the proteins from older animals are less susceptible to enzymic degradation than proteins from young animals."[5] This immunologic aging effect, however, may be significantly different than autoimmune reactions, perhaps a direct result of cross-linking between protein molecules and antibodies. The increase in the number of antibodies with age probably causes a gradual increase in this type of cross-linking damage.

The great variations in life-span between different species, however, is difficult to explain on an autoimmune basis. It is assumed that the somatic mutation rate is much higher in short-lived species, causing a more rapid immunogenetic diversification. When molecular biologists can measure or directly detect somatic mutations, they will be able to resolve many unknowns in both the somatic mutation and immunologic aging theories.

Immunologic theories cannot, of course, explain senescence

in animals that lack an immunologic system. However, it is also possible that mammalian aging has little in common with invertebrate aging.

Control of Autoimmune Disease

If the three-step process (cross-linking, somatic mutation, immunogenetic diversification) of senescence is correct, and immunologic aging is part of a pattern of progressive protein cross-linking deterioration throughout the body, then it may be controlled with the same therapy proposed by Dr. Bjorksten for breaking down all cross-linked molecule groups not digested by the normal level of enzymes—that is, daily hypodermic injections of an optimum mixture of suitable soil bacteria enzymes.

Assuming that the cross-linkages are difficult to break, or that somatic mutations are not caused by cross-linking, then any one or all of the conceptual means of correcting somatic mutations discussed in Chapter 8 would prove useful in controlling immunologic causes of aging.

If mutated lymphocytes are the principal villains, science should be able to eliminate such offending cells, though it is difficult to now say how this might be done selectively. No doubt progress in organ transplantation will provide many answers. Basic immunologic research in the next 10 to 20 years is likely to provide means of selective control that cannot be yet conceived within the framework of present knowledge.

If, however, autoimmunity aging is caused by mutation in all the cells of the body, control will be much more difficult. It might then be necessary to immunize the body's entire immunological defense system and supply the necessary antibodies against disease through supplemental injection. This would require truly massive but not impossible strides in biotechnology.

Antibodies are circulated in the gamma globulin blood fraction. Gamma globulin has been used in the treatment of such infectious diseases as hepatitis, polio and measles. Perhaps gamma globulin from young people could be administered to replace "old" gamma globulin as part of a complex anti-aging treatment.

A more satisfactory but as yet remote possibility would be to raise carefully controlled lymphocytes in tissue cultures. Advanced methods might make it possible to restrict antibody production to those lymphocytes which attack bacteria, viruses, and malignant cells. In addition to their possible value in aging control, the use of such carefully selected antibodies might be the final solution to organ transplantation and would revolutionize the treatment of bacterial and viral diseases. Indeed, the cure for all autoimmune diseases may lie in immobilizing the body's immunological system, followed by continuous replacement of antibodies from tissue cultures. Tissue-culture techniques are still somewhat primitive, however, and much basic research is necessary before their vast biological potential can even partly be realized.

With the elimination of the immunological system, in order to protect the body against disease, subjects would have to be placed in something resembling germ-free animal chambers. Advanced technology should someday make such protection possible. Perhaps pathogen-free environments the size of large buildings or even small cities could be perfected. In some experiments, feeding antibodies at low levels to conventional animals has rendered them qualitatively germ-free-like. Such treatment might be used to prepare people for entrance into pathogen-free environments.

Interestingly, a recurrent theme in classic science fiction stories during the 1920's and 1930's was man's achieving a great extension in life-span by living in a germ-free environment. Exotic applications for tissue cultures were also a staple of early science fiction. The germ-free story disappeared from science fiction when experiments with germ-free animals did not produce any longevity gains. Perhaps the early science fiction writers were accurate prophets after all.

For the present, however, autoimmunity and its relationship to cross-linking and cell mutations continue to concern scientists in search of a unified theory of aging. The three major theories have one important element in common—they all stress the action of individual cells throughout the body as the causative factor in the degenerative processes of senescence.

The next theory which we will consider, the cybernetic theory of aging, represents a new point of view in theoretical and experimental speculation about the aging process in that it explains senescence as organismal rather than cellular.

10

~~~~~~~~~~~~~~~~~~~~~~~~~~~~~~~~~~~~~~~

The Cybernetic Theory of Aging

"CYBERNETICS" is a word coined by the late Norbert Wiener to describe the science of control mechanisms. He defined cybernetics as "the entire field of control and communication theory, whether in the machine or in the animal." [1]

Dr. Joseph W. Still was one of the first scientists to recognize the importance of cybernetic information and decision theories in relation to biological systems. Dr. Still's cybernetic theory of aging [2] is unique in that it considers the nervous system—the vegetative brain in particular—as the key system. The vegetative brain is comprised of those centers that control all unconscious body functions. Thought or consciousness is restricted to other areas in the cerebral hemispheres which are located above the vegetative centers. Dr. Still's theory holds that the stable chemical parts of our brain neurons gradually undergo physical and chemical changes which cause them to become less and less capable of coordinating the rapid physiological adjustments to stress which are characteristic of youthful reactions. Aging is thought to be an indirect consequence of harmful molecular and other biological changes which result from this diminishing ability to adjust.

Dr. Still was an early adherent of the now generally accepted position that the nervous system and the endocrine system are not really separate systems but simply separate parts of the central control system by which the activities of the 30 to 50 trillion cells of a human being are kept in a state of harmonious cooperation. The nervous system provides direct cell-to-cell communication while the endocrine system communicates via chemical messengers (hormones).

According to the cybernetic aging theory, senescence is caused by increased transmission time in those brain nerve centers controlling the nervous-endocrine system. In other words, aging is the result of a gradual loss of control over all the cells in a complete organism. Dr. Still makes a sharp distinction between the death of individual cells and the death of the entire multicelled organism. The organism may be dead, as in electrocution, and yet for a few minutes none of the vital cells is dead. It is organismal and not cellular death that is to be prevented. Organismal death is believed to be due to disruption of vital control centers in the brain which serve to coordinate (through the nervous-endocrine system) all the activities of the body's billions of cells.

Dr. Still's theory makes it possible for science to approach aging as a disease. It is not easy to prove, however, that aging is caused entirely by increased transmission time in the brain centers controlling the nervous-endocrine system.

The cybernetic theory directly challenged the universally held belief that all chemical parts of human beings are being replaced by new chemicals every few years. If the cybernetic theory was correct, this belief in perpetual turnover had to be wrong.

To settle the issue, Dr. Still labeled some mice with a radioactive amino acid (C_{14} glycine). This was done by feeding the glycine to their mothers from the beginning of pregnancy until the young mice were weaned. All of the cells contained essentially equal amounts of the glycine. At intervals over the next six months, the mice were sacrificed and the radioactivity in their different organs measured. Organs such as the liver, kidneys and spleen which have constant turnover (replacement) of their cells rapidly lost all radioactivity. But cells in tissues, such as those of the brain and muscles, which are not replaced so rapidly remained radioactive. This important experiment not only gave considerable support to the cybernetic theory of aging, but it also overthrew a false belief about the chemistry of the body that was hampering progress in our understanding of the dynamics of the body at the cellular level.

Dr. Still believes that with the passage of time chemical changes take place in the stable parts of our brain cells which account for their gradual loss of reactivity. He speculates that these changes may be due to radiation damage or chemical cross-linkages, or simply to the gradual accumulation of molecular memory messages. Like a library that is overcrowded, the cells become so full of memory molecules that they have no room left to transact new business. If continued research proves that there is a buildup of permanent components decreasing the effective functioning of vital brain cells, then a search for internal bonding changes, which are thought to occur in aging brain cells, should prove fruitful.

There has been a sizable animal radiation program supported by the AEC and other agencies. It is highly doubtful that normal background radiation could account for aging. Doubling or tripling the background radiation dose does not significantly alter the life-span of experimental animals.

The suggestion that aging may be indirectly caused by an increased amount of stored memories in old brain cells would be somewhat distressing, because it might preclude any corrective therapy. Our present understanding of memory retention is useful in evaluating this possibility.

During 1966 considerable publicity was given to a new drug said to promote more rapid learning and better information retention in persons of all ages. Abbott Laboratories developed what is popularly referred to as the "intelligence pill" (magnesium pemoline), trade name "Cylert." It is currently being used by scientists to explore the biochemistry of learning and memory. Rats given Cylert learn four or five times faster than untreated rats and better retain what they learn. Preliminary Cylert experiments with humans are also encouraging.

At one time scientists believed that memory was recorded in the form of circulating electrical currents within the brain. This was not a complete explanation, however, since severe electric shocks and deep hypothermia that stops brain electrical activity do not destroy memory. The most recent research supports a molecular theory of permanent memory and thought, coupled with a modified electrical theory which accounts for short-term memory. This theory states that new information is first stored as circulating electrical signals which, in some unknown way, become permanent by altering the chemical composition of RNA (ribonucleic acid) molecules within brain cells.

According to this theory an increase in the rate of RNA synthesis within brain cells would improve learning and memory by speeding the electronic-biochemical process which causes information of thoughts to be transferred from temporary electronic retention to permanent molecular storage in new RNA molecules. Magnesium pemoline increases the rate of RNA synthesis by increasing the activity of the enzyme RNA polymerase through an as yet undetermined mechanism. If this explanation of memory retention is correct, then adverse chemical changes in the brain could not be caused by stored memories. The genius does not age faster than the moron. Nor is there anything in the aging patterns of lower animals to support the stored memory hypothesis. When more is known about electrical and biochemical thought-memory mechanisms, more refined approaches to the improvement of intelligence by chemical means will be possible.

One cannot discuss mind-altering drugs without mentioning

Aldous Huxley's unattractive prophecies in *Brave New World,* where "soma" completely tranquilized and controlled society. Mind-altering drugs are already available and future research should provide nonhabituating chemicals capable of creating any desired state of mind. Mind-altering drugs should not, however, be used by everyone. The illusionary paradise of soma might also produce a general complacency that would destroy ingenuity and innovation. A static unchanging society could be the result of altering our mental perception rather than correcting the shortcomings in our physical environment.

Dr. Still mentions cross-linkages as the remaining possible cause of adverse chemical changes within brain cells.

Cross-linking is a random phenomena. The rate is determined by temperature and the number of cross-linking agents in the body. Learning, however, does not occur at a constant rate. It tends to a cyclic activity with no relationship to the cross-linking rate. Moreover, animals given chemicals which increase the rate of cross-linking do not show any improved memory retention, though they do age faster. Therefore cross-linking cannot form the basis of memory retention within our brains.

Cross-linking does produce absolutely stable chemicals that cannot be excreted by any cells, including those in the brain. The accumulation of lipfuscin age pigments is a good example. If memory is retained through fine RNA molecular coding within our brain cells, then senility may be partially caused by cross-linking within and around these RNA molecules. The buildup of useless cross-linked debris would physically interfere with the RNA molecules holding essential memory data.

Though Dr. Still does not mention somatic mutations, they should be included in an evaluation of the cybernetic theory. Somatic mutations could account for the increased reaction time that disrupts the nervous-endocrine system. However, such somatic mutations would not be characterized by the buildup of absolutely stable material within the cells unless the mutations were caused by cross-linking. It might be argued that the increased reaction time is caused by somatic mutations that do not result in the accumulation of stable cross-linked materials, but the present experimental evidence is in support of the cross-linking explanation.

Dr. Bjorksten has observed: [3]

> Age changes in the total animal must exceed those in the cells. Those of us who have had anything to do with missiles know that, in a complex system, the reliability of the assembly declines much faster than the reliability of the individual components. This is a consequence of the probability of coincidence of flaws in the component parts.

Measurement of Nervous-Endocrine Change

Dr. Still has refined laboratory instrumentation that accurately measures endocrine-hormone changes in an active animal. His technique involves permanently implanting tiny tubes into the circulatory system of small animals. These tubes also extend outside of the animals. He first demonstrated that small polyethylene tubes (filled with saline solution), could be implanted into the aortas of rats and remain there indefinitely without hurting the animals.

The plastic intubation technique makes it possible to inject enzymes into the bloodstream of mammals. It can be used in large-scale experiments to break down cross-linked material in small animals. Hundreds of different enzymes or combinations of enzymes could be screened at one time. Such a program could start with existing enzymes and proceed to soil bacteria enzymes as they became available. One of the first applications of the polyethylene intubation technique was for hibernation research on small animals. Therefore my suggestion that hypothermia or artificial hibernation might be used to optimize the introduction of anti-aging enzymes into the body could be tested on hibernating animals or animals in hypothermia.

The intubation technique would enable scientists to measure nervous-endocrine changes in larger animals (dogs, pigs, etc.). A sizable number of small polyethylene tubes, implanted without destroying blood vessels or impairing circulation, would not be a source of stress. The multiple-tube automatic blood-collecting instrument has small plastic tubes which are extended to all the endocrine glands. The tubes project out of the skin on the animal's back where they are attached to a box that removes fluid samples from the freely moving animal. Dogs or pigs could be conditioned to the device from birth by having similar boxes strapped to their backs.

Dr. Still has devised an ingenious method for deciphering nervous-endocrine relationships whereby he can inject chemicals or remove fluid samples in any desired sequence. The control devices are connected to a coordinating system within the animal backpack. It should also be possible to radio-control the fluid sampling or drug injection at some distance from the moving animal. The system could be pre-programmed so that fluids could be withdrawn or drugs injected in any sequence that would elucidate nervous-endocrine relationships.

The multiple intubation system is applicable to many biomedical research areas which have only an indirect relationship to aging. It can be used in bioastronautic experiments in space to determine long-term effects of weightlessness. The system would also enable scientists to identify the changes in hormone output, enzyme processes and energy storage whereby hibernators reduce their life processes to a rate one-fiftieth of normal. It would be useful for nutrition and sleep research and in studying many chronic diseases. The system would also provide information important in refining the functioning of artificial organs. Multiple intubation permits long-range studies of pulse and blood pressure heretofore impossible.

The technique of studying brain electrical activity by implanting many small electrodes directly into animal brains is well advanced. If this technique were combined with Dr. Still's

multiple intubation system, scientists could electrically stimulate certain portions of the brain and accurately measure the
effect on the entire endocrine system. Perhaps the brain electrodes could have small companion polyethylene tubes for the
passage of fluids which would chemically stimulate the brain.
Many other refinements and additions are foreseeable. The
emerging art of microminiaturization will increase the sophis-
tication of this type of experimental equipment.

When we have a complete understanding of all the causes
of human aging, the cybernetic theory will probably be considered as part of an expanded cross-linking theory. Several
other aging theories, or subtheories, appear to be merging into
an all-encompassing cross-linking theory. One important gain
from the investigations centered around these compatible
theories is the development of ingenious experimental laboratory devices, such as Dr. Still's multiple intubation system.
Such devices will help perfect anti-aging therapies in a shorter
time period than would otherwise be possible and will play
an important role in elucidating the nature of all disease, its
prevention and cure.

11

Stress and Calciphylaxis

ONE of the most important questions in gerontology today is the extent to which environmental factors that cause disease also contribute to aging. Are causes of disease and senescence the same? Is there a direct or indirect relationship between them?

Dr. Hans Selye, the director of the University of Montreal's Institute of Experimental Medicine and Surgery, has done much work in exploring disease-aging relationships. Dr. Selye was born in Vienna in 1907 and educated in leading European universities. He moved to Canada in the 1930's. In 1936 he first presented his revolutionary concept of stress as a cause of disease. His imaginative research in subsequent years opened up countless new avenues for the treatment of degenerative diseases that usually accompany old age.

Dr. Selye includes in his stress theory an explanation for mammalian senescence. His description of the relationship between stress and disease is useful in understanding the stress theory of aging: [1]

> Stress is the rate of wear and tear in the human machinery that accompanies any vital activity and, in a sense, parallels the intensity of life. It is increased during nervous tension, physical injury, infections, muscular work or any other strenuous activity,

and it is connected with a nonspecific defense mechanism which increases resistance to stressful or "stressor" agents. An important part of this defense mechanism is the increased secretion by the hypophysis (another name for the pituitary gland at the base of the brain) of the so-called adrenocorticotrophic hormone (ACTH) which in turn stimulates the adrenal cortex to produce corticoid. . . . Various derangements in the secretion of these hormones can lead to maladies which I called "diseases of adaptation" because they are not directly due to any particular pathogen (disease producer) but to a faulty adaptive response to the stress induced by some pathogen.

The whole stress syndrome, or general adaptation syndrome (G.A.S.), evolves in three stages: 1. the "alarm reaction" during which defensive forces are mobilized; 2. the "stage of resistance" which reflects full adaptation to the stressor; 3. the "stage of exhaustion" which inexorably follows as long as the stressor is severe enough and applied for a sufficient length of time since the "adaptation energy" or adaptability of a living being is always finite.

The stress theory explains many diseases as caused by an overreaction by certain glands to temperature change, bacterial infection, injury and psychological trauma. Particularly important are the adrenal glands. Overproduction of these hormones, by altering organic metabolism or mineral metabolism, can have a harmful, sometimes fatal, effect on various organs. Diseases that can be wholly or partly explained by the stress theory include brain hemorrhage, hardening of the arteries, certain types of high blood pressure and kidney failure, arthritis, peptic ulcers and heart disease.

The stress-caused hormone overproduction pattern is different in each vital body system. Dr. Selye's explanation of the major cause of fatal heart failure is an example of one pattern. Physicians and the general public usually assume that blood clots are the cause of all fatal heart attacks. However, recent reviews of autopsies of people who died of heart attacks revealed no blood clots in 50 percent of the coronary victims, most of whom had died suddenly with no time lapse between a preliminary and subsequent fatal heart attack. The stress theory explains these deaths as caused by chemical changes which occur in the heart muscle.

Dr. Selye points out that potassium is the single most important chemical involved in maintaining normal heart function. Stress causes the adrenal glands to overproduce corticosteroid hormones which lower potassium levels in the heart. When potassium levels are reduced below the minimum required for normal heart function, the heart stops beating, causing sudden death.

Dr. Selye has conducted experiments in which rats, monkeys and other animals are given certain corticosteroids at the same time they were exposed to stress. All these animals died of heart attacks and none of them had blood clots in their coronary arteries. When the experimental procedure was altered by the addition of potassium chloride just before exposure to stress, the animals did not have fatal heart seizures. Dr. Selye has devised a preventative therapy for fatal heart disease that does not require a radical alteration of dietary or living habits. The therapy consists simply of a daily dose of potassium chloride.

Human tests with volunteers taking a measured daily dose of potassium chloride are underway in several countries. In the near future we should know if the potassium treatment does have a significant effect on the prevention of fatal heart attacks. Unfortunately human tests require a far longer evaluation period than do the results of animal experiments.

Hans Selye's brilliant insight into heart disease is an example of the way the stress theory can be used to explain the cause and possible prevention of disease in other vital tissues. There is no question that the stress theory will have a great impact on the prevention of certain degenerative diseases. Its impact on the refinement of a successful anti-aging therapy is less certain.

Dr. Selye observes that his stress theory may be a good starting point for speculation on the cause of senescence: [2]

> The general adaptation syndrome or "GAS," which develops under the influence of prolonged exposure to stress, exhibited many similarities to the syndrome of aging that evolves under the influence of prolonged living. Both appear to be related somehow to the necessity of constant adjustment and adaptation to the ever-changing requirements of existence. The term "adaptation energy" has been coined for that which is consumed during continued adaptive work, to indicate that it is something different from the caloric energy we receive from food; but this is only a name and we still have no precise concept of what this "energy" might be. Further research along these lines would seem to hold great promise, since here we appear to touch upon a basic property of living matter which decisively influences resistance to stress and hence to disease proneness at any age.

Dr. Selye points out that the triphasic pattern of the body's reaction to stress (described above) "is singularly reminiscent of the three stages of aging: 1) childhood, in which adaptability is great but adaptation still limited; 2) adulthood, during which the body has acquired resistance to most agents likely to affect it in life; 3) senility, with its characteristic exhaustion of resistance that is conducive to death."

The stress aging theory is really a sophisticated version of the old "wear-and-tear" theory of aging which holds that under constant use over a period of time every complex system, living or inanimate, literally wears out. The wear-and-tear theory cannot, however, satisfactorily explain the age-span differences between various species of mammals. Dr. Selye's concept of "adaptation energy" eliminates some of the loopholes in the older wear-and-tear theory.

Dr. Selye assumes that we are born with a fixed amount of adaptation energy. After exposure to a stressful situation, sleep and relaxation will almost, but not completely, restore the body to normal. Each stress event is assumed to use up a small amount of our adaptation energy reserve. Over the years these losses gradually cause aging.

Hans Selye believes that, to a large extent, the individual can control how fast he wants to use up his stored adaptation energy. According to the theory, one can use it up very slowly, being little more than a vegetable, but live a long life. Or one can live an energetic life full of stress which would be comparatively short. Of course, there is a middle ground between the two extremes, which is what Dr. Selye recommends.

Though the stress theory of aging centers around the concept of adaptation energy, there is no experimental evidence that such a thing as adaptation energy exists. Since the stress theory is based on a hypothetical substance that cannot be isolated or measured in the laboratory, further substantiation by experiments on mammals, or proof at the cellular level, will be required before the theory can be accepted. The gradually lowered resistance that characterizes the aging process can also be explained by cross-linking, somatic mutations or both.

Nor does the stress theory of aging satisfactorily explain the life-extension gains of McCay's rat experiments, though Dr. Selye has suggested that the necessity of metabolizing more than the optimal amount of food represents a constant stress which exhausts adaptation energy. There have been, however, a variety of animal underfeeding and caloric restriction experiments which would not fit Selye's explanation.

If there is such a thing as adaptation energy, can aging be slowed or even reversed by finding some means of renewing it? Hans Selye has speculated on this possibility: [3]

> Still, we have not fully excluded the possibility that adaptation energy could be regenerated to some extent, and perhaps even transmitted from one living being to another, somewhat like a serum. If its amount is unchangeable, we may learn more about how to conserve it. If it can be transmitted, we may explore

means of extracting the carrier of this vital energy—for instance, from the tissues of young animals—and trying to transmit it to the old and aging.

Though one cannot presently accept the stress theory as a complete explanation of senescence, Hans Selye's elucidation of the relationship between stress and disease is one of the most important medical discoveries of this century. Our overall goal of extended youth must include a complete understanding of all disease processes, particularly those which accompany the later stages of the aging process.

Calciphylaxis

Dr. Selye also discovered "calciphylaxis," which he defines as "a biological mechanism through which the organism can send large amounts of calcium and phosphate selectively to certain regions." He theorized that aging might be partly caused by a calcium shift from bones to soft tissue. There is really no direct relationship between calciphylaxis and the stress theory of aging except that they were both discovered by the same scientist. Calciphylaxis can be described in terms of the stress theory, but it can also stand as a completely separate explanation of aging.

One of the most common characteristics of old age is bone demineralization. Calcium, usually accompanied by phosphorus, moves from the bones into the soft tissues, such as the arteries, where it contributes to arteriosclerosis. There are calcium shifts to the connective tissues in the joints as well as to rib and larynx cartilage. Calcium shifts to the lens of the eye is one cause of cataracts. In each of these instances, the excess calcium causes the tissues to lose their youthful elasticity. Other minerals also accumulate in the soft tissue.

In 1961, after many years of research, Dr. Selye discovered that it was possible to selectively alter the rate of calcium deposition in the soft tissues. Calciphylaxis is the name for this artificial alternation of calcium shift patterns. This process involves a somewhat complex procedure which has, as yet, only been tried with animals. The first step is to give an animal a "sensitizer" agent which acts on calcium metabolism to produce a susceptibility to local tissue calcification. Parathyroid hormone and vitamin-D derivatives are strong calcium sensitizers. The substance most commonly used is dihydrotachysterol (DTH), a member of the vitamin-D group compounds.

The second step in calciphylaxis involves another group of chemicals called "challengers." After an animal has been given a sensitizer such as DTH, the challenger causes rapid calcification wherever it is directly applied or wherever it is deposited after being injected into the bloodstream. Most of the challenger chemicals are metallic salts, but some nonmetallic compounds such as egg white also act as challengers. In each calciphylaxis experiment, there is a critical time period which must elapse between administering the sensitizer and the challenger.

Each challenger works on a different set of organs, making possible selective calcification or complete petrification of the skin or a specific tissue. It is, for example, possible to paralyze an organ by encasing it in an internal wall of calcium. The organic selectivity of the challengers can be altered by attaching them to various organic compounds that serve as highly specific "carriers."

There have been several calciphylaxis experiments of great interest to gerontologists. Young rats treated with small daily doses of DHT developed the changes characteristic of senility. Within 60 days, they had calcium deposits in tissues which normally calcify at an advanced age. They exhibited marked skin wrinkling, hair and teeth loss, cataracts and wasting of muscle and sex organs, and had a greatly reduced life-span. They also exhibited the general pattern of physical deterioration associated with progeria, a rare human disease.

Progeria afflicts children and is characterized by retarded growth and the physical appearance and internal changes of premature senility. The skin wrinkles and there is extensive calcification of the arteries. The general pattern of changes described in the preceding paragraph occurs. The victims usually die of coronary disease before they are 30 years old. There is an adult form of progeria that occurs later in life.

Progeria is still a medical mystery. It does not precisely duplicate the pattern of normal senescence. Therefore the DHT calciphylaxis experiment which produced a progeria-like syndrome in young rats may not be true aging acceleration. However, many of the significant changes characteristic of senility were in evidence.

In another experiment, an identical group of young rats were given the same dosage of DHT that caused the progeria-like senility, but they were also given small daily doses of ferric dextran which prevented the premature aging. It appears that this iron compound, in proper dosage, attracts calcium so powerfully throughout the body that no single area can accumulate a large deposit. Ferric dextran and DHT together reverses calciphylaxis, an effect which Hans Selye calls "anacalciphylaxis."

Anacalciphylaxis eventually may be refined as an arteriosclerosis preventative therapy and might also be used to protect all of the soft tissues from excessive calcification.

In one impressive calciphylaxis experiment, a rat was sensitized with DHT and then egg white was used on its skin as the challenge substance. The rat's skin gradually assumed a rocklike hardness. After three weeks the rat began to shed its stony shell and emerged with young skin and hair. Though such an extensive molting process is not normal, it did not appear to hurt the animal. The rat was not rejuvenated, nor did he have an extended life-span.

Subsequent calciphylaxis-anacalciphylaxis experiments have demonstrated that a variety of anabolic steroid hormones which normally exert no obvious effect upon calcium metabolism will prevent the progeria-like syndrome in DHT treated rats.

Hormone replacement therapy can perhaps be expanded to prevent calcification of the soft tissues. A British research team recently reported that a newly discovered thyroid hormone, "thyrocalcitronin," sharply controls excess calcium in the blood by depositing it in bone. Thyrocalcitronin along with other hormones and anacalciphylaxis may be carefully combined as part of an anti-aging therapy preventing all soft tissue calcification.

The future role of calciphylaxis in degenerative disease treatment and prevention is likely to be a dramatic chapter in the history of medicine. Like hormone replacement therapy, it should extend the youthful portion of human life. Yet unanswered, however, is whether the migration of calcium from bones to soft tissue is a significant cause of senescence and whether calciphylaxis research will result in a modest or significant extension in mammalian life-span. Calciphylaxis research has not so far produced any life extension in experimental animals.

Future calciphylaxis research should contribute to the refinement of an optimum diet. Existing diets are known to contain substances which Dr. Selye identified as sensitizers and challengers and which would have, therefore, adverse effects on the organism, similar to those produced in calciphylactic experiments. Aided by the information from these calciphylaxis experiments, diets with a high synthetic food content, and controlling the proportions of sensitizer and challenger substances, should eventually be perfected.

People in cultures with significantly different diets show a lower incidence of certain degenerative diseases. Quite possibly the calciphylaxis effects of different foods contributes to this variance in disease patterns. Stress is also a factor. The stress pattern of a fisherman living on a tranquil Pacific island is radically different from that of a harassed business executive.

The causes of degenerative disease and aging are clearly related. Hans Selye has clarified the role of stress and calcium metabolism in disease and senescence. Calciphylaxis research should contribute to the refinement of anti-aging therapies based on other aging theories since calcium is bivalent and therefore a cross-linking agent. Calcium may even play a role in somatic mutations.

Calciphylaxis research has provided our first understanding and possible control of the disrupted mineral metabolism which accompanies senescence. Hans Selye has opened the research door to the precise control of all trace element concentration in our tissues.

12

~~~~~~~~~~~~~~~~~~~~~~~~~~~~~~~~~~~~

Cellular Therapy—Questionable
and Exotic

THE most controversial treatment against aging in recent years is cellular therapy discovered and refined by Switzerland's Dr. Paul Niehans. Though cellular therapy is most often categorized with such discredited therapies as testicle transplants, externotherapy, and ACS serum, it is still in vogue and presents some unanswered questions. There have recently been several books and numerous articles published describing "the Niehans treatment." Patrick M. McGrady, Jr., thoroughly reviews cellular therapy and other questionable anti-aging treatments in his new book *The Youth Doctors*.[1]

The analysis of cellular therapy in this chapter should be useful in helping to evaluate conflicting published material and to determine what information there is of scientific value to gerontologists.

Cellular therapy involves injecting humans with living cells from the organs of fresh animal embryos. In some cases these cells are injected within minutes after the embryo has been removed and dissected. Dr. Niehans contends that the body incubates these embryonic cells, keeping them alive to replace the life chemistry which aged human cells have lost. He believes that the chemistry in young embryonic cells is thousands of times as potent and active as the chemistry in adult cells, which slows down with the ravages of age.

Dr. Niehans describes cellular therapy as "a method of treating the whole organism on a biological basis, capable of revitalizing the human organism with its trillions of cells by bringing to it those embryonic or young cells which it needs. Cells from all organs are at our disposal; the doctor's art is to choose the right cells. Selective cellular therapy offers new life to the ailing or diseased organism." [2] The first series of treatments are directed toward "revitalizing all the organs afflicted by age," and when they are functioning normally, successive injections are administered to "strengthen the entire body by the revitalization of its sexual glands."

Paul Niehans states, "I do not rejuvenate, I revitalize." The revitalization treatment consists of embryonic genital cells, to which cells from the placenta are generally added. One of the goals of this treatment is to eliminate the arteriosclerotic modifications of the brain. The overall purpose of Niehan's revitalization is to "make all the organs struck by old age capable once more of functioning properly and at the same time bring fresh strength to the whole body by revitalization of the sex glands." For each impaired organ, "corresponding cells from a healthy organ."

Cellular therapy has been used to treat a wide variety of illnesses in addition to the degenerative diseases which occur with old age. Many astounding cures have been reported, which compounds the controversy surrounding the treatment. Niehans, however, excludes the following diseases as not "within the domain of cellular therapy." [3]

All virus diseases
All bacterial infections
Severely decompensated
  affections (heart)
Severe obstetrical traumatic
  lesions
Most benign and malignant
  tumors

The final stages of disease
  accompanied by severe
  destructive processes
All acute inflammatory
  conditions
Patients with disseminated
  septic foci
Hydrocephalus
Scar tissue

In his description of the treatment Niehans stresses that careful attention must be given to cell preparation procedures. The procedure is as follows: When the living embryo or fetus is surgically extracted, the organs are removed and placed in sterile Petri dishes filled with sterile Ringer's solution. They are immediately chopped up into ½ mm. pieces by means of special scissors. The tissue particles are then forced through a sterile sieve so that the suspended cells can be collected in a 20 cm. Record syringe and an intramuscular injection is made with a needle of 1.5 mm. diameter. Niehans emphasizes the importance of the quick transfer of the cells to the patient. There have been recent modifications in the method of injection.

It should be mentioned that the Soviet Academician Filatow developed a cellular treatment based on the same principle as Alexander Bogomoletz's ACS serum. Filatow used dying cells, not vital embryonic cells. He believed that dying cells secreted substances that stimulated growth in the remaining body cells. Niehans always stressed that his approach was significantly different from Filatow's therapy, which is no longer used in the USSR.

The Placebo Effect

The validity of cellular therapy has been almost entirely discounted by the Anglo-American scientific community. Very few technical books on gerontology mention Niehans or his treatments. Niehans' critics are unanimous in attributing the benefits of cellular therapy to "the placebo effect," a label it has in common with other discredited rejuvenation treatments, testicular transplants, externotherapy and ACS serum.

It is well known that a high percentage of the cases of male sexual impotency are caused by psychological factors. Since mental decline can accelerate senile decline, it is not surprising that cellular therapy, which fosters a positive attitude, will be useful in the treatment of impotency.

The placebo effect is reinforced by the procedures involved in the therapy. The patient is confined to bed for three days before the cellular injections and must remain in bed for three additional days. Tobacco and alcohol are prohibited for at least one month. The patient follows a nutritionally excellent diet and avoids any overexertion. Since most of the people who come for these treatments lead hectic professional and social lives, these beneficial changes in their routines immediately create a sense of well-being. Moreover, Dr. Niehans, a commanding, aristocratic figure, inspires great confidence and the patient believes that the treatment will be of great value.

Cellular therapy is most popular in Germany where a number of clinics specialize in this treatment. Other cellular therapists operate in France, Scandinavia, Egypt, and Mexico. For the most part, these cellular therapists, including Niehans, do not publish their records in a conventional statistical manner, so the results of cellular therapy cannot easily be determined.

The validity of any anti-aging treatment must eventually stand or fall on its ability to extend the life-span of animals in carefully controlled experiments. It should be possible to prove or disprove the claims of cellular therapists by means of mice that are so imbred that they have no immunological rejection response to tissue transplants between members of this single genetic strain. Since the usual immunological barriers would not exist, the full effects of the injections of various embryonic cells into adults could be evaluated. Radioactive tracers within the embryonic cells would be useful in determining the fate of injected cells.

Niehans rediscovered cellular therapy in 1931. He received worldwide publicity in 1954 when Pope Pius XII was brought back from a near-fatal illness by his treatments. Despite the widespread Anglo-American criticism of Niehan's treatments, no one in the United States or England has conducted the requisite experiments to prove or disprove the claims of the cellular therapist.

Unquestionably many quacks have engaged in cellular therapy and have given the field a dark reputation. However, it should be stressed that serious research is going on in the field, primarily centered in Germany. Responsible German scientists such as Dr. Joachim Stein and Dr. Fritz Schmid have engaged in cellular therapy investigations. Their results have been published in a monograph, *Cell Research and Cellular Therapy*, which has recently been translated into English.[4] This volume is the most extensive review of recent cellular therapy research available to the scientific community. There is also a journal on cellular therapy published in Germany.

Cellular therapy will remain extremely controversial until the effectiveness of the treatments can be fully established. If the cellular therapists are interested in scientific accreditation, they should collectively finance the proof-of-principle animal experiments which would discount the possibility of the placebo effect.

Cellular Replacement—An Exotic Possibility

Although cellular therapy may be completely ineffective, its basic theory may be partly correct or at least contain the outline of valid ideas. Some speculative concepts about a future form of cellular therapy made possible by advanced biotechnology deserve consideration.

We have noted that one explanation of the longevity of the sturgeon and giant tortoise is that the cells of all their organs, including the central nervous system, never stop dividing. This represents a form of built-in cellular therapy. Their vital organs are slowly but continuously being resupplied with new cells. Tissues with dividing cells are "youthful" because they are composed almost entirely of new vital cells. Continuous cell division compensates for the loss of cells rendered defective by mutation or progressive cross-linkage.

Since humans are subject to a fixed adult size, the cells in vital organs stop dividing. Niehans' cellular therapy suggests future research options which should enable us to duplicate the rejuvenation effects of continuous growth without actually stimulating growth.

The bulk of research evidence suggests, however, that embryonic transplants from another species would be quickly rejected. When foreign tissue is transplanted into the human body, antibodies are produced which destroy the foreign tissue in two or three weeks. The greater the genetic difference, the stronger the immunological reaction. Though embryonic tissue transplants from the same species are tolerated surprisingly well, in some cases for months, they are eventually rejected.

In experiments at the Royal Marsden Hospital in London, bone marrow cells taken from premature stillborn babies thrived when injected into adults. Clearly, therefore, human embryo bone marrow cells injected into humans will combine with the adult bone marrow and multiply. Bone-marrow cellular injections from unrelated donors have saved the lives of people receiving what would normally be a fatal radiation exposure. This form of cellular therapy may become a standard treatment for intense radiation.

American scientists have cured a type of inherited anemia in mice by injecting fetal liver cells into the adult mice. The new cells restored normal blood production in most of the anemic mice, enabling the animals to live to a healthy old age. It should be noted that all these experiments used embryonic cells from the same species.

The Niehans treatments generally use embryonic lamb cells, though in some cases pig and calf cells are used. Niehans considers human embryonic cells superior to animal cells, especially in the treatment of sugar diabetes, and regards human pancreas cellular injections as a "sovereign" cure for this disease. He observes: "If the law gave us the means to utilize all human foetuses aborted medically, we would have many more diabetics definitely free from insulin." [5]

Experience with organ transplantation and bone marrow

injections suggests, however, that the entire immunological system would need to be extensively suppressed by radiation or drugs for human embryonic cells to survive indefinitely. The danger is that the body's defenses against disease would be severely weakened to the point where minor bacterial infection could cause death.

Since the immunological transplant barrier does not exist between identical twins, the problem becomes one of creating an embryonic twin of the person to be treated (i.e., that the injected cells be genetically identical to the other cells in the body). There are two exotic possibilities in human reproduction which would produce identical twin embryos of adult men and women. Twenty years ago the French scientist Jean Rostand removed rabbit ova, stimulated them into beginning embryonic development, and then placed them in host female rabbits. These foster mothers subsequently gave birth to normal rabbits who had had only one parent. In this process, called parthenogenesis, the offspring received a double charge of heredity from one parent. Dr. Rostand extended single parenthood to the male. He extracted the material chromosomes from rabbit ova, introduced a rabbit sperm cell, and embryonic development proceeded with the father's chromosomes alone. This process is called androgenesis and could theoretically permit a man to be the sole parent of millions of children.

Let us now see how parthenogenesis and androgenesis might be used in cellular replacement. For the woman, some years of preparation might be required. Ova could be extracted during youth and frozen for a number of years. The use of glycerol or dimethyl sulfoxide (DMSO) as a biological antifreeze has had some initial success in freezing mammalian ova. When the time came to start the anti-aging treatments, the following procedure would take place.

A frozen ovum would be taken out, properly warmed and the preservative glycerol or DMSO removed. Then it would be stimulated into beginning parthenogenetic embryonic growth and placed in the uterus of a "host" mother. After the proper number of weeks had passed the embryo would be aborted or surgically removed. All of its vital organs would be quickly separated and prepared for a number of separate cellular injections. The cells would be introduced into the body in a manner deemed best for migration to their corresponding organs. The remaining embryonic cells might be frozen with DMSO until needed at a later time.

Women produce a comparatively small number of ova during their reproductive years whereas men produce billions of sperm. The woman's problem might be answered by two other exotic possibilities. The first is superovulation, a recent reproduction achievement. Special hormones injected into cattle cause as many as 100 ova to ripen at one time. The mass ovulation is followed by artificial insemination, and several days later the embryos are removed by surgery and reimplanted directly into the uteri of other cows where they grow to term. Thus one pedigreed cow can be the parent of thousands of calves. The superovulation technique could be applied to women at the present time. Several hundred ova would be produced for anti-aging cellular therapy over a number of years.

The other possibility was also suggested by Jean Rostand in his fascinating book, *Can Man Be Modified?*: [6]

> By means of a fine pipette, the nucleus—that is to say chromosomes—is removed from a frog's egg. Then another nucleus is introduced, taken from one of the many cells that compose a frog's embryo. The egg that has been completed afresh in this way develops regularly and yields a normal creature, with a chromosome make-up strictly similar to that of the donor embryo, so that it will be a sort of "retarded twin" of the latter, rather than a real descendant.
>
> The main interest of this experiment is that it shows that any of the numerous nuclei of the embryo can set in motion the development of the egg. It proves that any of these nuclei possesses the genetic value of a germinal nucleus.

Rostand's comments suggest that a single ovum might be extracted from a young girl, stimulated into parthenogenetic development and then separated into thousands of individual cells which could later be used to create new embryos for cellular replacement.

For the male, there is no shortage of sperm. Ova could be denucleated, the sperm introduced, thereby starting androgenetic embryonic development. The embryo would be placed in a host mother with the subsequent procedure identical to that used for women.

Sex in humans is determined by the X and Y chromosomes in male sperm. All the cells in a woman, except ova, contain two X chromosomes. Ova ready for fertilization have only half (23) the regular number (46) of chromosomes and always have one X chromosome. An ovum stimulated into parthenogenetic development doubles the 23 chromosomes to a full 46, which now includes two X chromosomes. Since women only carry the genetic blueprint for their own sex, all parthenogenetic embryos would be female.

All the cells in a man contain X and Y chromosomes except sperm. It is the Y chromosome that is decisive and establishes maleness. The sperm each contain 26 chromosomes, and have either an X or Y chromosome. If a sperm cell with an X chromosome fertilizes an ovum, a female develops. If a sperm cell with a Y chromosome fertilizes an ovum a male develops. Half of all androgenetic embryos would be male, half female. Since only the male embryos would be suitable for cellular replacement in men, it would be desirable to separate the male and female sperm, an achievement which may soon be realized.

A Russian woman biochemist, Dr. V. N. Schroder, claims to have perfected a successful method which controls the sex of offspring. She reports that a magnetic field in a saline solution made male-producing sperm (with a Y chromosome) migrate first to the positive pole, and female-producing sperm (with an X chromosome) migrate first to the negative pole.

Laboratory tests were only 80 percent accurate, but perfect results may be obtained by a new device that takes only the first sperm cells to arrive at the positive and negative poles. Such a technique would be useful in cellular replacement for men, cutting in half the number of human embryos that would need to be produced.

Basic biological research may make it possible to bypass the sperm and ova in the development of embryonic identical twins for cellular replacement. Except for the red blood cells, all of the cells of the body have an identical set of chromosomes each with a genetic blueprint for another complete organism—an identical twin of the person from whom the cell would be taken.

In order to grow a complete embryo from random mammalian cells, it will first be necessary to learn how to control the chemical repressors ("histones") which determine how a cell grows. Histones are "on-off" biochemical switches. When these molecular switching functions are understood, it should be possible to create as many identical individuals as desired.

With the exception of red blood cells, it is believed that every cell in the human body contains seminal potential. The rapidly dividing cells of older people would be the logical choice because they would most likely have discarded cross-linked material and the mutated cells would not have survived in competition with their youthful neighbors. There remains the problem of the proper means of introducing the genetically identical embryonic cells into the body. Some cellular therapists believe that the animal cells or cell structures migrate to their respective organs through the lymphatic system. Cellular therapists do not actually inject single cells, but tiny clusters of cells, which Niehans contends separate into individual cells once they begin to migrate from the point of injection.

Scientists have perfected methods of separating embryonic mammalian cells. The binding matter which holds cells together can be removed by treating them with a calcium-removing agent and then placing them in a weak solution of the enzyme trypsin, a loosening agent. For certain tissues other enzymes or enzyme combination are required. The separated cells can be placed in a tissue-culture nutrient for subsequent cellular replacement injections.

The interesting result of experiments with dissociated embryonic cells is that, under appropriate conditions, the cells come together and form structures typical of the organ they were orginally a part of. Kidney cells form small tubules; cells from limb buds form lumps of cartilage surrounded by muscle tissue; dissociated heart cells coalesce into rhythmically contracting tissue. The Israeli biologist Dr. A. A. Moscona has demonstrated that dissociated embryonic cells from different species (mouse and chicken) would intermingle and form a common mosaic organ structure. Dr. Moscona's brilliant concepts have been the key to most dissociated cell experiments. Cellular therapists frequently cite his work to support their claims. Dr. Moscona is optimistic concerning the potential of dissociated embryonic cells to function in the receptor organism: [7]

> Recent experience indicates ... that dissociated cells may exhibit their inherent powers of self-recognition and organization in the living organism as well as in culture fluids. In 1952 Weiss and G. Andres injected a suspension of pigment-forming skin cells from one breed of chicken into the bloodstream of chick embryos of an unpigmented breed. Pigmented skin and feathers appearing on these chicks demonstrated that the injected cells had become localized in the skin and resumed their normal development. Thus an organism devoid of a certain type of cells has been "seeded" with them by injection!
>
> Such experiments have given reality to hopes that the loss of cells or tissue in adult organisms may, in certain cases, be restored by injection of a suitable cell suspension. Important progress in this direction has been made in studies of animals exposed to X-rays. Exposure to intense radiation destroys the blood-forming tissue in the bone marrow and causes death. The injection of viable bone-marrow cells greatly increases their

chance of survival. The injected cells become lodged in the depleted bone marrow and reconstruct blood-forming tissue there. It is even possible to replenish destroyed marrow with cells from another species. Bone-marrow cells from rats have been successfully transplanted by injection into irradiated mice. These promising experiments are receiving considerable attention in view of their obvious medical implications.

The idea of tissue synthesis from dissociated cells thus presents ever more challenging possibilities to the biologist and medical investigator.

In the Weiss-Andres chicken experiment, the dissociated cells were injected directly into the bloodstream. In the human organism, however, the injection of a large number of cells might block some of the small capillaries in the brain and kidneys. Therefore, the cells could perhaps be slowly introduced into the bloodstream over a period of several hours, using intravenous feeding techniques.

It might be best to inject the dissociated embryonic cells directly into the thoracic duct of the lymphatic system. The lymphatic system is the second circulation system in the body. Almost as extensive as the bloodstream, it collects and returns to the bloodstream vital fluids that leak out of the capillaries. Lymph nodes produce some of the white cells that are part of the immunological system. Since cell migration is common in the lymphatic system, it may be the ideal means of circulating the newly injected cells.

Even if the dissociated cells are introduced into the bloodstream, some thought must be given to the lymphatic system. Adverse changes may occur in the immunologic system causing it to attack normal body tissue (see Chapter 9). A runaway immunologic system might also attack the migrating dissociated embryonic cells.

Immunosuppressive drugs might be given prior to cellular replacement anti-aging treatments. Another possibility would be to pass the lymphatic fluid outside the body and remove the offending white cells or destroy them with radiation. The latter technique has been used for kidney transplants. The thoracic duct is severed and connected to a loop of plastic tubing which extends outside the body and is then passed back to the other severed end of the thoracic duct.

The refinement of suitable means of introducing dissociated embryonic cells into the body should not be too difficult. It is doubtful that they would need to be injected directly into their respective organs. More likely, the bloodstream will be the avenue of transport.

Now we come to the most difficult requirement of cellular replacement—making room for the new cells in the aging organs. Chapter 7 described the process by which dying cells are replaced by fibrous connective tissue largely composed of cross-linked collagen. This increasing mass of inert tissue would prevent the dissociated embryonic cells from effectively joining the vital portions of important body organs. The only solution to the connective tissue barrier is to break up cross-linked protein—particularly collagen. A youthful connective tissue should allow the replacement cells to fill in the gaps left by dying cells.

Though there are substances which will prevent cross-linking in newly formed collagen, we have nothing that will break up old, heavily cross-linked collagen. *It is doubtful that cellular replacement can be successful without first perfecting means of ridding the body of cross-linked protein—particularly collagen.* Dr. Bjorksten's cross-linking theory and proposed therapy utilizing soil bacteria enzymes may be the key to slowing down the aging process and also may provide the essential requirement for rejuvenation through cellular replacement.

Cellular replacement could assume a particularly important role in anti-aging therapy if somatic mutations cannot be prevented or controlled by some of the methods discussed in Chapter 8. It is conceivable that all of the permanent cells of vital organs, including the brain, may be slowly replaced over a period of many years.

Parthenogenesis, androgenesis, superovulation, and the other means of preparing suitable embryonic dissociated cells are sufficiently advanced so that the process could be applied to humans in three to five years' time. An effective means of mobilizing old cross-linked protein is the only remaining basic research requirement. The possibility of cellular replacement is another strong argument in favor of accelerated research on means of ridding the body of cross-linked material. Dr. Bjorksten's proposed therapy remains the most important goal to be achieved before man can control the aging process.

Assuming that cellular replacement therapy is one day completely successful, the next step might be ectogenesis, or test-tube pregnancy. An English biologist, the late J. B. S. Haldane, originally predicted the advent of ectogenesis in *Daedalus,* written in the early 1920's. He was a friend of the late Aldous Huxley who used the theme of ectogenesis in his prophetic novel, *Brave New World.*

An Italian surgeon, Dr. Daniele Petrucci, claims to have taken human ova and placed them in a plastic womb where they were fertilized with human sperm. Plasma from a number of pregnant women was used to give the embryo nutrition, and oxygen was supplied by hyperbaric techniques. Dr. Petrucci reports that he has been able to grow human embryos through 59 days of fetal development in this artificial environment. The Petrucci experiments have not, however, been duplicated by other investigators and many scientists are skeptical about Dr. Petrucci's report of two months of human ectogenesis.

Mammalian embryos have been grown for several days in an artificial environment. Scientists have kept aborted fetuses alive for two days in a 200 psi hyperbaric chamber, forcing oxygen through the skin of the developing fetus. But these experiments still require a means of removing carbon dioxide and other wastes.

The proposed use of parthenogenetic and androgenetic human embryos for cellular replacement would, of course, face extremely severe legal and religious objections in most Western countries. The proof-of-principle experiments must first be made on animals before human parthenogenesis and androgenesis are attempted.

The proposals in this section are presented for thoughtful reflection. Unforeseen physiological complications may also prevent the realization of these proposals. For example, dissociated embryonic cells could cause cancer, though there has been no evidence of malignancy from embryonic tissue transplanted into humans and animals. To guard against the possibility of cancer, the cells could be checked for signs of malignancy before injection. The dissociated cells would not be kept in a tissue culture medium long enough to start any changes resembling malignancy.

It is important to remember that these proposals do not support contemporary claims of Dr. Niehans and his followers. Cellular therapy uses small clusters of cells, not dissociated cells. Cellular replacement would use cells genetically identical to the person treated, not cells from another species.

Cellular replacement, still far from general acceptance and widespread clinical application, represents one of the most exciting prospects for the control of senescence. Should this treatment be perfected, it would provide an effective means of controlling the aging process and one which takes into account all of the theories we have considered thus far.

13

~~~~~~~~~~~~~~~~~~~~~~~~~~~~~~

Other Theories and Therapies

THE reader has already been presented with what may seem to be a bewildering array of aging theories. One recent gerontology monograph listed 120 different explanations of senescence. Most of them were subtheories; some were discredited historic theories such as Elie Metchnikoff's proposal that aging is caused by bacterial toxins produced in the colon. As Alex Comfort so accurately remarked: [1]

> In almost any other important biological field than that of senescence, it is possible to present the main theories historically, and to show a steady progression from a large number of speculative, to one or two highly probable, main hypotheses. In the case of senescence this cannot profitably be done.... It is a striking feature of these theories that they show little or no historical development; they can much more readily be summarized as a catalogue than as a process of developing scientific awareness.

Many of these theories or subtheories include a rationale for anti-aging therapeutic additions to our increasingly complex "elixir of life." Though in almost every case they can be explained by one or more of the principal theories described in preceding chapters, they also cover other aspects of senescence.

Temperature and Senescence

Sixty years ago, Dr. Max Rubner proposed that aging can be explained as a consequence of the rate of energy expenditure in our tissues. Rubner found that the total lifetime energy expenditure per gram of tissue during adult life is roughly constant for several species of domestic mammals. "The higher the metabolism the shorter the life-span and vice versa."

The first experimental evidence in support of Rubner's theory was found in 1917 by Dr. Jacques Loeb and Dr. John H. Northrop (1946 Nobel Laureate in Chemistry). They showed a clear relationship between life-span and the temperature at which fruit flies were kept at a certain stage of their development. This was the first demonstration that environmental manipulation could produce a considerable increase or decrease in the life expectancy of a highly complex organism. In these fruit fly experiments, Dr. Northrop also found that the period of growth could be prolonged by starvation for various periods of time. This set the stage for McCay's dietary breakthrough 16 years later.[2]

Rubner's theory would partly explain the great life-span differences between large and small animals. Body heat loss is primarily a surface phenomenon. The surface-to-volume ratio of large animals is much lower than that of small animals. Consequently, a large animal can maintain the same body temperature as a small animal with a lower metabolic expenditure. It has been estimated that both men and mice expend approximately 726 calories per gram of tissue over their lifetimes. The ratio of calories given off per kilogram of body weight per day is:

25.5 calories	1 kilogram for man
170 calories	1 kilogram for mice

It is interesting to note that women expend 23.2 calories 1 kilogram each day which is 2.3 calories 1 kilogram lower than the metabolic rate for men. This metabolic difference, according to Rubner, accounted for the fact that women live, on the average, three years longer than men.

Rubner's original metabolism calculations were based on observations of five domestic animals (cat, dog, pig, cow and horse). However, these mammals do not have a close evolutionary relationship to one another and they vary in size. Shortly after Rubner published his findings, other scientists pointed out that there were large disparities in average life-span between like-sized mammalian species.

Rubner's theory would suggest that man's closest relative, the gorilla, should be the longest-lived primate. Yet man's average life-span is almost twice that of the gorilla. In fact the comparatively smaller chimpanzee lives as long or longer than the gorilla—about 30 to 35 years. The chimpanzee and young gorilla have about the same metabolic rate as man.

The sperm whale is another mammal not accounted for by Rubner's theory. These large animals live in warm water and are protected from heat loss by a thick layer of blubber covering their entire bodies. Their life-span has not been firmly established but it is probably not more than 30 to 50 years.

The sperm whale has the largest well-developed brain of any mammal. Some scientists have tried to correct discrepancies in Rubner's theory by relating brain size to the energy expenditure calculation. But sperm whales do not appear to live longer than the smaller-brained California gray whale which is almost the same size.

Birds do not fit Rubner's theory. A canary has a higher metabolic rate than a mouse, but its life-span is 7 times longer.

McCay's rat experiments are not explained by Rubner's theory. There was no significant metabolic reduction in the underfed rats. Their total calories given off per kilogram of body weight was much higher on a lifetime basis than that of the fully fed controls.

Forcing animals to increase their metabolism appears to shorten the life-span. Rats kept in a cold environment had to increase their metabolism by 30 percent in order to maintain normal body temperature. Their life-span was decreased and all causes of death were accelerated.

Without question the rate of metabolism has some effect on life-span. The explanation is most likely to be found in one of our major aging theories. For example, a higher metabolic rate would increase the number of cross-linkages throughout the body, as well as the somatic mutation rate. Roy Walford's speculative three-step process (various agents causing cross-linking, cross-linking causing somatic mutations, somatic mutations causing immunologic aging) might also be increased by a rise in metabolism.

The mechanism at the molecular level by which cross-linkages are broken down by enzymes, or somatic mutations corrected, probably differs between various species. This difference would account for the life-span disparities between like-sized mammals.

Metabolism is important to experimental gerontology even if it only acts as a moderator for the rate of cross-linking. Control of metabolism could be one means of favorably extending the life-span. It has already been mentioned in Chapter 6 that artificial hibernation may play a role in enabling temperature-sensitive enzymes to break down cross-linked protein. Some thought should be given to metabolism reduction by itself as a means of life-span extension.

Dr. Robert S. de Ropp was impressed by the comparatively long life-span of creatures that hibernate every night. The hummingbird, for example, with its extremely high metabolic rate must hibernate every night in order to survive. Various species of hummingbirds live between 8 and 12 years. The species of small bats which hibernate while they sleep have life-spans 8 to 10 times longer than like-sized nonhibernating mammals.

Dr. de Ropp believes that hypothermic sleep is a promising means of extending the life-span: [3]

> Man could add perhaps twenty-five years to his life if he could learn the hummingbird's trick and cool down at night. Metabolism falls with temperature and at 68° F., is only 25 per cent of normal . . . [heart] load could be reduced to one quarter of normal value . . . the length of life of this vital organ would be prolonged.
>
> It can be safely assumed that all other organs would profit similarly by the rest. The vital enzyme systems of the body would be spared the denaturing effects of high temperatures.
>
> Hypothermic sleep has been ignored by the gerontologists, which is most unfortunate because it represents one of the most promising means of experimentally prolonging the life span.

Dr. Henry Swan of the Research Institute for Biological Studies in Denver, Colorado, may have discovered a way for man to approximate hibernation. Thyroxin, produced in the thyroid gland, is the most important hormone regulating the rate of metabolism and exercises a catalytic effect on oxidation processes throughout the body. Dr. Swan speculated that the balance of nature would require a substance to hold thyroxin in control, an antithyroid compound that would neutralize thyroxin.

Dr. Swan was able to isolate his antithyroid substance from African lungfish. During long, dry summers, African marshes become caked mud flats. Lungfish survive by aestivating (a form of natural reduced metabolism similar to hibernation but without any drop in body temperature). Large African lungfish secrete a gelatinous material which becomes a hardened cocoon. Their metabolic rate falls to 15 percent of normal, a state they can maintain in the tropics for almost two years. In this case it was obvious that metabolism is suppressed chemically, not by temperature.

Dr. Swan prepared extractions from the mid and hind brain of the African lungfish. These extractions were rendered essentially fat-free and then injected intravenously into white rats causing a 30 to 40 percent reduction in the rats' oxygen intake and CO_2 production. This metabolic reduction was accompanied by only a slight fall in body temperature.

Dr. Swan calls the antithyroid substance "anabolone." Anabolone may provide the key to human hibernation, and it is likely to have a revolutionary impact on many other fields of biochemical investigation, including research in cancer, shock, fatigue, sleep, and the aging process. Anabolone could revolutionize the clinical treatment of high fever, trauma, heart failure, infection, and cerebral vascular accidents.

Additional research is still necessary to further purify anabolone extractions and to determine its effects on animals other than the lungfish. Should it be found, as a result of more refined experiments, that anabolone does promote longevity in other animals, it would be valuable to explore the relationships of metabolic rate to cross-linking and somatic mutations.

The continuous introduction of a small amount of anabolone would result in a slightly reduced metabolism rate. The shrew would be well suited for such experiments, since it is the smallest mammal and has the highest metabolic rate. The shrew must consume more than three times its own weight in food daily to maintain its high metabolism. The continuous introduction of small quantities of anabolone might significantly extend the life-span of shrews and other experimental animals. As such experiments became more refined, the relationships of metabolic rate to cross-linking and somatic mutations could be explored.

Protein Synthesis

Some gerontologists contend that senescence is primarily caused by changes in the structure and function of tissue proteins. There is a high turnover in protein molecules both inside and outside the cells. Any interference in the rate or effectiveness of new protein synthesis could be a cause of aging. The synthesis of altered or faulty proteins might also contribute to biological decline.

Cross-linking or somatic mutations can result in the production of an altered activating enzyme, which in turn causes alterations in protein molecules vital to the complex processes of living tissue. Some insect experiments suggest that such a process contributes to insect aging, though as mentioned before, the pattern of senescence in insects and mammals may be significantly different.

The best solution to reduced protein synthesis or faulty protein synthesis is to correct the primary cause. If it is cross-linking or somatic mutations, the therapies outlined in Chapters 6 and 9 might be applied. However, these anti-aging remedies are not yet perfected, and interim measures would be necessary.

Dr. G. A. Usbekov of the I. P. Pavlov Ryazan Medical Institute in the Soviet Union has refined a comparatively simple anti-aging therapy based on the protein synthesis hypothesis. Certain compounds of sulfur and hydrogen (sulfhydryl groups) are essential components of many tissue proteins and enzyme systems. With senescence, renewal and reproduction of these protein molecules slow down. In some cases trace elements such as cadmium block sulfhydryl-containing molecules and enzymes. These proteins are also subject to oxidation during normal metabolic activities.

Usbekov reasoned that an increase in the number of sulfhydryl groups available for new protein synthesis would partly offset the deactivation of sulfhydryl-containing molecules. For his experiments he used a simple solution of hydrogen sulfide dissolved in water. Young rats given the hydrogen sulfide from the time they were 3 months old were larger and healthier than the controls. They enjoyed an average life-span extension of 21.4 percent over the controls. Usbekov also found that small doses of hydrogen sulfide given to older rats (starting when they were 16 months old) increased longevity and resistance to disease. Unfortunately Usbekov used a small sample of animals, and experiments using a large number of rats will be necessary to provide more reliable evidence.

Dr. Simion Oeriu of the Department of Chemotherapy at the Academy of the Rumanian People's Republic in Bucharest has proposed a therapy similar to Usbekov's approach. He theorizes that as the body ages, there is a change in the ratio of the amino acids cystein and cysteine. A high level of cystein facilitates the incorporation of sulfhydryl groups into new protein molecules. Dr. Oeriu believes that a "youth cocktail" containing cystein along with vitamins that boost its effect (B_6 and B_{12}), would mitigate some of the effects of aging.

Oxidation and Free-Radical Theories

A number of scientists have speculated on the role of oxygen in the aging process. Dr. Aloys S. Tappel of the University of California at Davis has proposed an "oxidation theory of aging." He believes that excessive oxidation of polyunsaturate fats produces a high level of free radicals which causes molecular damage including cross-linking of vital proteins. The system within the cells that normally breaks down and excretes damaged cellular components is also impaired by the free radicals. Some damaged cellular components accumulate and become lipofuscin age pigments.

Dr. Tappel proposed a mixture of antioxidant nutrients as a preventative therapy. These nutrients include vitamin E, vitamin C, sulfur amino acids and micro quantities of selenium. Vitamin C has a synergistic relationship to vitamin E, increasing its antioxidant properties. Selenium replaces sulfur in amino acids, producing selenoamino acids which are extremely effective antioxidants. Dr. Tappel's explanation of aging can fit into an expanded cross-linking theory. The attractive feature is a preventative therapy that can be started at the present time.

The free radical theory of aging was first presented in 1956 by Dr. Denham Harman of the University of Nebraska. Dr. Harman believes that aging may in part result from biological damage caused by free radicals formed both inside and outside the cells. Free radicals are unstable molecular fragments which last only a few thousandths of a second before they react with nearby molecules and form chemically stable bonds. Free radicals are powerful cross-linking agents. The intracellular damage can be explained by the somatic mutation theory, though free radicals formed outside the cells could not cause somatic mutations.

Free radicals most likely do the greatest damage to the organism through cross-linkage, including somatic mutations caused by DNA cross-linkage. A smaller portion of free-radical damage may result from somatic mutations that are not caused by cross-linkage.

Dr. Harman agrees with Dr. Tappel that polyunsaturated fats are particularly susceptible to being catalyzed into forming free radicals. The life-span of experimental mice was reduced by feeding them excessive quantities of polyunsaturated fats.

A major factor in free radical formation is the presence of metallic catalysts (trace elements) within the tissues. Dr. Harman found that copper is a particularly damaging catalyst. One approach to life-span extension, therefore, would be to avoid water with a high copper level or to take drugs which remove copper from the system. When the role of other trace elements in free radical formation is better understood, drugs can be taken to reduce them to relatively harmless levels.

Dr. Harman's most dramatic experiments have employed chemicals which neutralize free radicals before they can react with the vital molecules in the tissues. These chemicals, called antioxidants, were originally developed to minimize radiation damage, which is partly caused by free radical formation.

One antioxidant, 2, 6-di-tert-butyl hydroxytoluene (BHT) was able to increase the half survival time (age at which 50 percent are dead) of mice by 50.3 percent over the controls. This would be equivalent to increasing the average human life-span from 70 years to 105 years. However, the BHT experiment is not conclusive because the controls did not live as long as they normally do, which seemed to be the result of synthetic food the mice were fed.

Dr. Harman now has experiments under way that should correct the dietary deficiencies and provide conclusive evidence of the anti-aging effects of antioxidants. There are some new antioxidants that promise to be as effective as BHT. These experiments are extremely important because they promise to provide the first effective anti-aging therapy that could be easily taken by the general public.

A variant on the oxidation theory has been proposed by Dr. Efimov, director of the Respiratory Laboratory of the Soviet Ministry of Health in Moscow. According to Dr. Efimov, aging is a process of slow suffocation or gradual asphyxiation, perhaps akin to emphysema, caused by progressive deterioration of the lungs. The result is that less oxygen is absorbed in the alveoli of the lungs.

Dr. Efimov maintains that the lungs function more efficiently at higher mountainous altitudes. For people who remain at lower altitudes he suggests rapid walking, running, or swimming, followed by a quarter of an hour's rest. There are other explanations of senescence (Chapter 8) which suggest that an increased quantity of oxygen favors longevity. Periodic sessions in small hyperbaric chambers, perhaps during the hours of sleep, may be the best technological solution to the oxygen supply problem.

A modification of the oxygen availability theories might be called the "circulatory failure" theory. That is, as we age the small capillaries tend to break down, causing localized anoxia (lack of oxygen) throughout the body. The anoxia kills individual cells, which are replaced by scar tissue with a high collagen content. The scar tissue tends to shrink in time and choke off more capillaries causing more anoxia—a vicious cycle of progressive tissue destruction. The circulatory failure of small capillaries probably causes many of the symptoms of aging. Anoxia has also been proposed as one possible cause of cancer.

Small capillary breakdown, an aging phenomena peculiar to mammals, is probably caused by cross-linking of protein molecules within the connective tissue of the capillaries. Cross-linking may also promote the formation of small deposits of capillary-blocking calcium.

Howard J. Curtis suggests that somatic mutations in the endothelial cells of the capillary walls is the cause of the breakdown of that part of the capillary. Curtis points out that these endothelial cells are "known to undergo division from time to time, and cell failure by mutation is more probable with cell division. Further, it only takes failure to one cell to block a capillary." [4]

Excessive oxidation of vital proteins, decreased oxygen supply, and capillary breakdown resulting in local anoxia may all be secondary causes of aging. The primary causes, as mentioned in preceding chapters, are probably cross-linking and somatic mutations.

Autointoxication

The autointoxication theory maintains that certain nutritive substances are necessary for life, but toxic if consumed in quantity. Vitamin D is a good example. We cannot survive without it, but an excess of vitamin D will cause the adverse changes observed by Selye in his calciphylaxis experiments.

An improper balance between the different amino acids is

thought to be a cause of autointoxication. Dr. R. B. Fisher calculated that if the diet normally given to rats contains sufficient amounts of all essential amino acids, then the rats are consuming a toxic quantity of the amino acids tyrosine, phenylalanine, and tryptophan. If future research determines that the autointoxication effect is significant, then the refinement of synthetic foods may offer the final solution. The accumulation of lipofuscin age pigment granules within the cells may also be attributed to autointoxication. It is assumed that the buildup of these pigments is caused by improper metabolism of nutrients within the cells as well as by cross-linking.

The Integrated Theory of Aging

The goal of a composite theory of aging that will adequately explain all causes of senescence has been frequently mentioned in preceding chapters. Denham Harman has commented: [5] "The people proposing aging theories remind me somewhat of the story of the seven blind men examining an elephant; to the one feeling a leg, an elephant was like a tree, the one feeling the trunk thought he was like a big snake, etc.—each being correct so far as he went. So with the aging theories, each is probably correct to a certain extent."

Donald G. Carpenter and his associates at the U.S. Air Force Academy are currently refining an "integrated theory of aging." Though in the preliminary stages, and subject to modification and change, it appears close to the goal of a complete elucidation of senescence.

In the integrated theory, cross-linking of all types of molecules (not just proteins, enzymes, DNA and RNA) is assumed to be the major cause of aging. The rate of cross-linkage is increased when the organism is subject to stress (chemical changes in the system are responsible). The cross-linked molecules are divided into two groups—genetic and nongenetic.

The cross-linking of collagen and similar nongenetic molecules would affect the organism's total molecular efficiency, causing it to decrease. The diffusion of oxygen, hormones and nutrients into the cells and excretion of waste products would be hindered. The total molecular efficiency would also be decreased by the accumulation of waste products not caused by cross-linkage.

The cross-linkage of DNA produces somatic mutations, but mutations are also produced by other causes. The effect of the mutation is ramified by immunologic reactions which are, in turn, increased by distortions in the control or system feedback between the central nervous system and the endocrine glands (cybernetic theory).

Cross-linkages, mutations, immunologic reactions and cybernetic considerations (loss of control) acting together reduce the minimum efficiency of the sum total of the body's molecules required for survival. The minimum level becomes higher as the number of mutations increases. The difference between the organism's total molecular efficiency and the minimum required for survival is a measure of the organism's ability to withstand stress. Whenever the stress encountered exceeds the organism's ability to withstand the stress, the organism dies.

Figure 5, page 197, presents a schematic view of the integrated theory of aging. This is a highly simplified picture and does not cover every detail. For instance, immunologic changes may cause additional cross-linkages which in turn could accelerate the entire pattern of progressive decay. Somatic mutations could halt the production of intracellular enzymes which normally break apart cross-linked molecules.

Dr. Carpenter stresses the fact that his integrated theory, as outlined in this book, has not been published and "exposed to the fluorinic fury of the entire academic community." However, its foreseeable importance is so great, that a "preview summary" is presented with the understanding that the integrated theory will probably be subject to certain modifications.

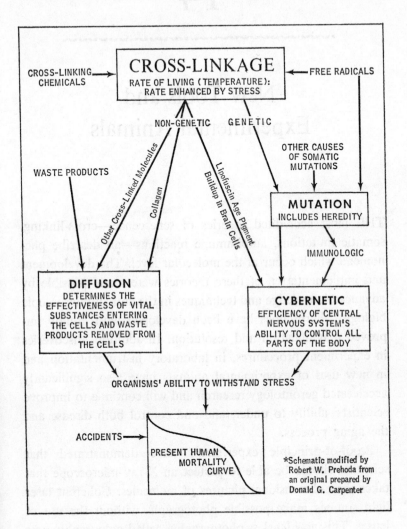

Figure 5. Integrated Theory of Aging.*

14

New Tools and
Experimental Animals

THE most accredited theories of senescence—cross-linking, somatic mutations, autoimmune reactions—all describe phenomena which occur at the molecular level. The development and implementation of these theories were made possible by advanced knowledge and techniques in the area of microscopic biology. Microscopes have been developed with greatly improved magnification and resolution. In addition, discoveries in experiment procedures, in laboratory instrumentation and in new uses of experimental animals have also significantly accelerated gerontology research and will continue to improve scientists' ability to understand and control both disease and the aging process.

Proof-of-principle experiments have demonstrated that scientists should be able to perfect an X-ray microscope that takes three-dimensional pictures of molecules. Coherent laser light sources make possible photographs without the use of lenses. This new lensless photography, called holography, uses wave-front reconstruction which operates by "freezing" the field pattern of the light waves as they exist on a plane in space. The frozen pattern of the lines and whorls appear as random patterns, but are used to reproduce recorded light waves exactly as they would have appeared to the eye. Consequently the images reproduced from the wave recordings are three-dimensional images. Holography can record images formed by waves that cannot be focused with lenses, including X-rays, and can magnify images as much as one million times.

A powerful laser X-ray microscope would add a new dimension to biomedical research and molecular biology by making possible motion-picture observation of the innermost life processes. Three-dimensional pictures of living molecules would greatly help scientists to unravel their exact structure, and to better understand the chemistry of biological processes and the relationships between complex molecules and other organic chemicals. An X-ray microscope would also be of great value in synthesizing hormones, enzymes and other biological compounds.

Laser photography is applicable to other areas of the electromagnetic spectrum. It might make possible an improved variation of the ultraviolet, color-translating, television microscope. Since various chemical substances in the cells absorb ultraviolet light at different wavelengths, the television microscope uses three light sources from different portions of the ultraviolet spectrum to activate the red, blue, and green elements of a color television tube. This process produces magnified pictures of living cells in which various chemical components appear in different colors, thus making possible identification of life substances through color contrasts. A system using laser color holography should produce far better resolution, at the same magnification, than can be achieved through conventional television scanning.

Scientists at Toulouse, France, have built a formidable electron microscope (78 feet long) which photographs living bacteria. The microorganisms to be examined are enclosed in a tiny air-filled cell with collodion film windows (less than four-millionths of an inch thick), on the top and bottom. A large accelerator sends a focused beam of million-volt electrons through the collodion films, producing shadow pictures of the bacteria magnified 25,000 times. Advanced versions of this type of electron microscope system might eventually be used in controlled genetic modification experiments, a possibility first suggested by Sir George Thomson.

When fully developed, the huge electron microscope at Toulouse will operate at 1.8 million volts (MV). The French have a 3 MV electron microscope in the design stage. A much more advanced instrument of 5 MV is being discussed in the United States. A 10 MV electron microscope is within the realm of technological refinement. Such instruments will probably be more than 200 feet in length, and will provide a view of molecular processes unobtainable in any other way.

Germ-free Animals

Techniques have been perfected for raising animals under germ-free conditions. Also called axenic animals, they are brought into a sterile chamber at birth by means of complex Caesarean operations. Monkeys, mice, and other animals spend the rest of their lives in cylinders that are microbe-free, breathing filtered air and eating sterilized food. The animals are handled with long rubber gloves which are sealed to openings in the cylinder. The older all-metal cylinders are being replaced by germ-free isolators with walls of transparent flexible vinyl film.

Proper nutrition has been one of the most difficult problems in the raising of germ-free animals. The solution seems to lie in synthetic diets administered from birth, in which each nutritive substance is synthesized in absolutely sterile conditions. Such diets would be useful in certain immunologic aging experiments. Progress is being made in developing synthetic food for germ-free animals. Three generations of axenic mice have been raised on a water-soluble, sterile diet consisting only of readily absorbable compounds: purified amino acids, glucose, vitamins, and minerals.

As mentioned in Chapter 10, the greatest problem with

germ-free animals is enlargement of the cecum, a blind pouch that opens into the upper part of the large intestine. The most common cause of death among older germ-free animals is a rupturing of the cecum, an occurrence unrelated to the aging process. The paper-thin walls of the enlarged cecum allow toxic substances from the lower bowel to diffuse into other parts of the animal. Such autointoxication could also result in a variety of age acceleration changes. These metabolic toxins may increase the rate of cross-linking in germ-free animals.

Surgical removal of the cecum may be one solution. The introduction of a single strain of bacteria (clostridium difficle) into the intestinal tract has reduced cecum size. The manipulation of electrolyte balance in the large intestine is another experimental approach to cecum enlargement.

Once the cecum problem has been overcome we will be able to determine how much longer germ-free animals live compared to controls. Germ-free mice with enlarged cecums lived approximately 10 percent longer than contaminated controls. One surprising observation is that germ-free males live longer than germ-free females, a reversal of the usual pattern among mammals.

When present problems in maintaining axenic animals have been solved, they will become a useful tool in every sector of experimental gerontology. Axenic animals will be particularly useful in nutrition research and immunologic aging studies, and will make it possible to determine the precise effect of a single nutritive element, drug or germ on the organism.

One particularly intriguing experimental possibility is to duplicate McCay's underfeeding experiment using germ-free animals fed on synthetic food. The quantities of the individual nutrients could be varied to determine the nutrient combination that results in the greatest longevity.

The basic germ-free isolators and related technology can also be used to raise pathogen-free animals which are contaminated with harmless bacteria but are isolated from microbes that cause disease. Because the cecum does not become enlarged in pathogen-free animals, they are presently more suitable for aging research than germ-free animals. The maintenance and handling precautions for pathogen-free animals are less strict, an economic advantage.

Radiation-free Animals

The projected success of raising germ-free animals fed on precise synthetic diets suggests an even more exotic experimental subject: the radiation-free, germ-free animal. The technique of tracing organic compounds within living organisms is well advanced. Radioactive isotopes are incorporated in the compounds and their path and evolution are followed with radiation-detection instruments.

The quantity of any compound used in this way is limited by the "background noise" produced by the radioactive elements in living tissues. This background radiation presents both quantitative and qualitative limitations on biological radioelement experiments.

Our tissues contain three isotopes of potassium. Two stable isotopes, potassium-39 and potassium-41, account for almost 99 percent of the total. The remaining 0.0119 percent is comprised of the unstable isotope potassium-40 which is responsible for most of the radioactivity within our bodies.

Potassium-40 can be separated from the nonradioactive isotopes of potassium through high-speed-rotation liquid metal centrifuges. Other radioactive isotopes, including carbon-14, can be separated from nonradioactive carbon-12 by gaseous diffusion of methane gas, the same technique used to produce uranium-235. Isotope separation technology will make possible the production of radiation-free synthetic food, enabling animals to be raised with less than one-hundredth of the normal internal radiation levels. These animals could be shielded from atmospheric fallout from nuclear weapon testing by being in a completely closed ecological system that used advanced technology transfer from space life support systems being developed for manned planetary expeditions. Such a system would also keep out radioactive tritium (hydrogen-3) which is produced in extremely small quantities by cosmic rays. Thick lead and massive water shielding around the animals would exclude almost all radiation from the earth and cosmic sources.

The availability of radiation-free animals will help scientists explore and better understand ionizing radiation and somatic mutations. Radiation causes biological damage, but the precise mechanism of such damage is still the subject of debate. Background radiation is not, however, believed to be a significant factor in mammalian senescence.

Radiation-free animals would also aid in the refinement of radioisotope biological experiments. One might compare them to a new microscope with a magnification 100 times greater than conventional instruments. The very smallest quantities of any organic substance would be traced through the body and its exact final disposition determined. Animals composed only of stable isotopes could provide a considerable amount of information on the physiological effects of excessive ionizing radiation, a subject of increasing importance in this age of nuclear development and space exploration. Radiation-free animals would also be important in elucidating suspected synergistic relationships between radiation and viruses in cancer.

New Experimental Animals

One of the greatest problems in many aging experiments is that the scientist must wait until all of the experimental animals have died before final results can be determined. For instance McCay's underfeeding experiments required a minimum of 1,465 days, the life-span of the longest-lived rat. All age extension experiments are up against a comparable problem.

The most obvious solution is to conduct experiments on animals with shorter life-spans. In 1962 Dr. Roy L. Walford and Dr. William H. Hildemann undertook a field expedition to a remote part of Brazil where they obtained specimens of a unique short-lived annual fish, *Cynolebias adloffi,* with an average life-span of about 1 year. These fish show characteristic signs of senescence as they age and so are used in aging experiments.

Though fish are vertebrates, it is desirable to use more highly developed animals. The shrew is the smallest mammal and is believed to have the shortest life-span, between 1 and 2 years. When more is known about these tiny animals, their use would shorten the time necessary for aging experiments.

A ready supply of aged experimental animals is a major requirement of experimental gerontology. It should be possible to establish a number of centers where rats, dogs, pigs, monkeys, and other suitable animals of known life cycles, heredity and physiology are available in large numbers. Automatic feeding and pen-cleaning technology could reduce cost, and eliminate, for the most part, the need for human attendants. These "pathogen-free" animals would be particularly suitable for aging research. Germ-free and radiation-free animals could be provided at a considerably greater expense. It is important that the less exotic of these animal colonies be set up as soon as possible. Dr. Alex Comfort observes: "Failure to deal with the animal logistics problem will hinder research in ten or twenty years time, and that hindrance could be avoided by forethought."

The small size of some animals makes surgery difficult in many experiments. The answer has been to use larger animals, usually dogs, which are available in quantity. Actually the dog is not a very good experimental animal. It does not survive surgery as well as humans. Moreover, dog lovers have made organized efforts to prevent the use of dogs for these purposes;

antivivisection legislation has hindered biological research in many areas.

A small pig, a strain called the Pitman-More miniature, has been specially bred for medical research. The pig is closer to man from a physiological standpoint than the dog. Both develop a similar pattern of arteriosclerosis in their cardio-vascular systems. Like man, they will adjust to a diet composed of any variety of animal or vegetable food components. Pigs are extremely hardy creatures and are more likely to survive radical research surgery than cats, dogs, or monkeys. However, their comparatively long life-span of about 15 years is a limitation to their use in aging experiments. If a large colony of Pitman-More miniatures was started now, properly aged pigs would be available for a variety of anti-aging experiments in the late 1970's.

Dr. Harry Sobel has proposed the use of the pigmy marmoset for aging research. These South American monkeys are the smallest living primates. They always give birth to identical twins, which provides built-in controls for aging experiments. The pigmy marmosets have an average life-span of 8 to 10 years.

Animals which might be described as "freaks of nature" show promise for use in aging research. The opossum, an American marsupial, is unusual in that it gives birth to its young about 12 days after conception. At the time of birth, the young are embryonic and can be compared with a 10-week-old human embryo. In the 60 to 70 days after birth these primitive mammals grow through embryonic, fetal and infancy stages similar to the development of human young. During this entire development they are carried in the mother's pouch, providing ready accessibility for experimental manipulation.

Dale L. Carpenter has developed techniques for removing and returning these young embryos to the mother's pouch. He also developed an artificial pouch in which the young embryo can be nurtured and grown apart from the mother. The artificial pouch permits great flexibility and control of the embryonic opossum fetuses for a variety of biomedical experiments.

Research conducted by Dale Carpenter included exposure of opossum embryos to hormones, irradiation, varying nutrition and other experimental parameters. By being able to conduct research in the earliest formative stages of an embryo without disturbing its environmental parameters (possible with marsupial embryonic fetuses, but not yet possible with intrauterine embryos and fetuses), we can discover the basic mechanisms of the beginnings of aging, which occurs as soon as a cell, tissue or organ is established as an entity.

The aging research in cross-linkage of proteins can also be begun in early embryonic stages when enzymes are first being produced. Even minute changes instigated during embryonic stages will result in gross differences when the embryo has become an adult. Thus the opossum embryo can act as a biological amplifier. Early administration of irradiation, hormones, pharmaceuticals, anti-aging enzymes, etc., to opossum embryos or fetuses will provide insight to the causes and prevention of aging in man.

There is another, somewhat exotic means of providing perfect control animals for all biological research. Parthenogenesis and androgenesis (see Chapter 12) would produce as many identical duplicates of any mammal as desired. The genetic characteristics of such animals would be exactly the same throughout the animal colony. Even highly inbred strains of animals cannot duplicate this degree of genetic replication.

Parthenogenesis and androgenesis could be refined in the near future to provide perfect controls for all the experimental animals of interest to gerontologists: mice, rats, hamsters, opossums, dogs, pigs, pigmy marmosets and other primates. Experimental animal populations of exact genetic uniformity would be of great value to all branches of biomedical research.

Specialists from many disciplines contribute to experimental gerontology. Instruments devised by the engineer and other technologists play vital roles in aging research. Aided by the ecologist, the search for new experimental animals should be intensified. Many scientists who have given little thought to experimental gerontology may offer unexpected proposals that will be useful in man's battle to overcome the limiting chains of senescence.

15

~~~~~~~~~~~~~~~~~~~~~~~~~~~~~~

Sex and Senescence

WE live, more than ever, in a youth-conscious and a sex-conscious world. The close association between sex and senescence in the minds of men is age-old (see Chapter 1). The medieval alchemists were correct in their basic reasoning that an effective anti-aging therapy should also extend sexual capacity.

Two different sexual problems are caused by the aging process: the decline of sexual potency in men; and physical appearance—skin wrinkling and loss of body firmness—in women. In the area of male potency it is extremely difficult to separate fact from fantasy. Physicians frequently state that 90 percent of all cases of impotency are due to psychological problems. But surely the multiple physical disabilities of advancing senescence must considerably alter this ratio in older men, particularly those past 70.

Many factors can have an adverse influence on virility. Psychological considerations are important. Declining sexual capacity is often due to a general loss of vigor. Many severe illnesses which do not actually damage the sexual organs result in a diminished sexual capability after recovery.

This "side effect" of disease mirrors the pattern of reduced virility produced by senescence, both primarily involving energy loss. The extension of youth through anti-aging therapies, therefore, by increasing basic energy reserves, will also enhance virility.

One prevalent fallacy is the belief that overindulgence in sexual activity exhausts nerve centers in the sexual organs. This idea is probably a holdover of the Victorian belief that middle-aged men become impotent because of their great promiscuity in youth. In fact, the opposite pattern seems to be emerging from our present understanding of changes in virility with age.

Our understanding of the relationship between sex and senescence has been somewhat restricted by the fact that there has been relatively little reliable research on the subject. For many years sex was a taboo subject for scientific inquiry. It is to the everlasting credit of the late Dr. Albert C. Kinsey that this barrier was broken in 1948 with the publication of *Sexual Behavior in the Human Male*. The past 20 years have witnessed an avalanche of articles and books covering one or more aspects of sex.

There are some severe limitations in the basic approach used by Kinsey and his imitators for purposes of determining the relationships between sex and senescence. Most of the studies of sexual patterns have relied on the interview and questionnaire technique whose findings are not, therefore, scientifically verifiable.

Many scientists have compiled voluminous information about sex, but only a few have attempted physiological measurements of actual human sexual activity in the laboratory. Now that barrier has been overcome. In 1966, *Human Sexual Response* was published. The authors, Dr. William H. Masters and Virginia E. Johnson, reported on over 10 years of laboratory observation of humans engaging in a wide variety of sexual activities. They used advanced laboratory instrumentation, including color motion-picture cameras, EEG and EKG attachments, along with many special devices allowing a better view and measurement of sexual response. Three hundred and ninety women and 315 men participated in the laboratory phases of the investigations. It is not surprising that the book quickly became a best seller, even though it was strictly a scientific monograph using medical terminology and written in the style of a technical paper.

The male and female subjects who participated in the Masters-Johnson experiments covered a wide age-span, the oldest being an 89-year-old male. The findings of these experiments offer the best available data on sexual changes accompanying senescence.

Masters and Johnson found that "mental rather than physical fatigue is the greatest deterrent to male sexual responsiveness, although both are capable of major influence in lowering or aborting sexual tension." They attribute the high incidence of mental fatigue to the fact that most men in the 40-to-60-year age range are engaged in the most intensively competitive phases of their careers, when financial pressures and family emergencies often accelerate.

Their results also confirmed the importance of regular exercise in maintaining virility. Masters and Johnson found that the older male whose job involves considerable physical activity will have a steady sexual pattern. The sedentary male or the "weekend athlete" usually experiences "a reduction in or complete loss of sexual responsiveness during the 24 to 48 hours immediately following unaccustomed physical effort." There have been other investigations showing that a sound program of regular exercise significantly increases virility in older men.

Masters and Johnson examined the role of nutrition in sexual response. It has long been known that excessive consumption of either food or drink, particularly alcohol, will suppress sexual appetites. Proper nutrition promotes good health and a high energy level, though no single vitamin or combination of vitamins has been found to cure impotency.

Other scientists have investigated the potential of hormone replacement therapy in correcting impotency in older men. In cases where a decline in hormone output was the principal cause of loss of virility, artificial sex hormones were sometimes administered with spectacular success. But sex does not depend on hormones alone. Every physiological cause of senescence must be considered and controlled if we are to completely restore a youthful virility level.

Masters and Johnson report changes in specific sexual response as the body ages, but observe that sexual capability is frequently maintained to an advanced age: [1]

> As the male ages, the major differences in sexual response relate to the duration of each of the phases of the sexual cycle. As opposed to the younger man's well-established reaction pattern of immediate erection, early mounting, and rapid ejaculation, the older man (particularly over 60 years old) is slower to erect, to mount, and to ejaculate. The resolution-phase refractory period also lengthens for the male past the age of 50 years.
>
> If there has been a well-adjusted marital pattern of frequency of coital exposure, it usually is maintained well into the fifties by healthy males.
>
> With rare exceptions the male over 60 years old usually will be satisfied completely with one or, at the most, two ejaculations a week regardless of the number of coital opportunities or the depth of his female partner's sexual demand. Many men in their middle or late fifties and in their sixties find that they cannot redevelop penile erection for a matter of 12 to 24 hours after ejaculation. Those who achieve a relatively early return to erection may have lost their ejaculatory urge and are perfectly content to serve their female partners to the completion of the woman's sexual demands without recurrent ejaculatory interest.
>
> There is every reason to believe that maintained regularity of sexual expression coupled with adequate physical well-being and healthy mental orientation to the aging process will combine to provide a sexually stimulative climate within a marriage. This climate will, in turn, improve sexual tension and provide a capacity for sexual performance that frequently may extend to and beyond the 80-year age level.

Many men in their 70's and 80's are capable of intercourse. There is a decline in the level of sperm production, but not a complete cessation. Preliminary evidence suggests that a surprising number of men at an advanced age are still capable of reproduction.

The frequency of advanced paternity presents questions relative to the sex and senescence factors involved when older men have young wives. Older male rats live longer if they are groomed by young female rats. Is there a comparable effect in humans? Here we are primarily dealing with specific psychological factors that influence the rate of aging.

Experimental gerontology promises that senescence will some day be slowed, possibly halted, maybe even reversed. All mental and physical capabilities associated with youth will be favorably modified, including male sexual potency and virility. The elixir that rejuvenates will also be a potent aphrodisiac though its most important effect will be maintaining a high energy level. Anti-aging therapies will also directly affect the sexual organs, slowing or preventing any tissue alternation that would diminish sexual capability.

Older women are not confronted with declining sexual potency. Some adverse physical changes can be corrected by hormone replacement. The woman's most serious problem is the physical deterioration of aging, skin wrinkling and loss of muscle tone.

Dermatologists point out that there is considerable evidence indicating that too much sun actually *speeds* the aging process in the skin. Continuing exposure over the years causes irreversible changes in the deeper layers of the skin. The skin's connective tissue too may be damaged and permanently stretched until it loses its elasticity. "It seems clear," says Dr. John Knox of Baylor University, "that the onset of skin degeneration is independent of age, being determined simply by the cumulative amount of injury from ultraviolet light. The visible cutaneous changes usually interpreted as aging are apparently due largely, if not entirely, to sunlight."

Skin wrinkles are believed to be caused by cross-linking of collagen and elastin in skin connective tissue (see Chapter 7). The loss of hyaluronic acid, which has an ability to hold water, also plays a role in wrinkling. Collectively these factors cause the connective fibers of the skin to move closer together, reducing the turgidity of the skin and resulting in wrinkles!

The corrective anti-aging therapies discussed throughout this book hold forth the exciting promise of restoring the appearance of a youthful skin by making the skin physiologically youthful though complete rejuvenation of the skin may never be possible.

The restorative effects of face-lifting and other forms of cosmetic surgery usually last only about five years and the surgery cannot be repeated more than two times. Quite possibly anti-aging therapies would extend the years of cosmetic surgery effectiveness by slowing the rate at which the skin ages after surgical modification.

Anti-aging therapies would greatly improve muscle tone and body firmness by preventing the loss of individual muscle cells and retarding the buildup of cross-linked collagen in the connective tissues. It is not unreasonable to expect that all adverse connective tissue changes may eventually be controlled, allowing the physical appearance of youth to be retained throughout an extended life-span.

Sex in the Age of Extended Youth

The experimental gerontologists will be victorious. The twenty-first century will surely witness the beginning of the age of extended youth. The control of senescence will forever alter sexual patterns in an advanced society.

Advances in gerontology will probably be accompanied by progress in plastic surgery. Twenty-first-century cosmetic surgery should make possible significant changes in face structure, including alterations of racial characteristics. Breast enlargement will be refined with lifelong safe prosthesis that will look and feel natural. Already it is possible to shorten or lengthen bones in the legs. Cosmetic surgery will be performed without detectable scar tissue. Obesity can be eliminated by injections of suitable fat-mobilizing hormones.

The age of extended youth will of course also include very long life-spans. Extended life-spans will have a decided effect on marriage. Some couples could stay married for a century or more. Is there a "boredom barrier" that will preclude life-long marriages? Will the institution of marriage be retained as we now know it?

The traditional age-determined roles in society will be changed. Today, most of the adult years are spent raising and educating children. In the age of extended youth only a fraction of the adult years will be devoted to the upbringing of children.

By the end of the third century of life, a person could have two or three thousand direct descendants. What would be the relationship with distant descendants? Robert A. Heinlein explored this question in the science fiction classic *Methuselah's Children* (first published in 1940).

In the twenty-first century, parthenogenesis, androgenesis and ectogenesis could result in radical changes in human reproduction which in turn would have a profound influence on sexual patterns. One individual could be the sole parent of a child. Ectogenesis would make the woman's role in reproduction similar to that of the male.

Anti-aging treatments for extending youth will also correct the sexual dilemmas associated with senescence. The influence of an extended life-span on future sexual patterns can only be dimly foreseen. It is certain, however, that psychological problems influencing sex will be lessened when the vigor of youth is combined with wisdom gained through a long lifetime of fruitful experiences.

16

The Gerontology Funding Dilemma

IT must be stated boldly that experimental gerontology is not receiving even a fraction of the research money needed for optimum progress.

To understand the almost criminal neglect of gerontology funding, it is useful to review the way the Federal Government organizes and supports all biomedical Research & Development. After taking a brief tour of the Byzantine labyrinth of Federal life science support and neglect, I hope that you will share with me my deep sense of concern.

The total American expenditure for all R&D will be over $24 billion in 1968. Approximately $6 billion will be financed by corporations, foundations and other segments of private enterprise. The Federal Government will support over $16 billion in R&D throughout all government agencies. In recent years, approximately 10 percent of Federal R&D funds have been spent on all life science R&D programs. The division of biomedical R&D funds from private and government sources during the past few years is shown in the table on page 216.

It should be mentioned that a considerable portion of the private biomedical research in pharmaceutical companies is directed toward obtaining patentable variations of products already marketed by their competitors. Other life science de-

NATIONAL SUPPORT FOR MEDICAL RESEARCH, 1948 – 1968*
(Obligations in millions)

Source of funds	1948	1953	1958	1963	1964	1965	1966	1967 est.	1968 est.
Total	124	214	543	1,436	1,652	1,841	2,057	2,280	2,490
Government	50	108	292	964	1,099	1,229	1,377	1,523	1,670
Federal	50	107	279	919	1,049	1,174	1,316	1,458	1,601
State and local	n.a.	1	13	45	50	55	61	65	69
Industry	43	58	170	375	400	450	511	580	640
Private support	31	48	81	147	153	162	169	177	180
Foundations and health agencies	19	26	45	85	88	92	94	100	101
Other private contributors	n.a.	n.a.	6	21	22	25	28	29	30
Endowment	12	15	19	19	19	19	19	19	19
Institutions own funds	n.a.	7	11	22	24	26	28	29	30

*Covers only medical and health-related research; such activities as research training and construction are not included.
Beginning with 1962, data for non-Federal components have been improved and are not strictly comparable with those for prior years.

velopment expenditures are running around $400 million, resulting in a R&D total around $2 billion. The development funds are heavily committed to aircraft and spacecraft life support research requirements, with only modest commitments to development of systems for biological research and medical requirements. It must be recognized that, as in other R&D fields, these funding totals include very expensive overhead for personnel in the organizations administering grants and contracts or conducting research. Reliable estimates indicate that less than $1 billion is actually spent on biomedical research after these overhead costs and administrative expenses are subtracted.

An analysis of the breakdown of government biomedical research funds shows that the National Institutes of Health (NIH) has over half of the biomedical R&D funds. The breakdown of biomedical R&D funds between government agencies in recent years is shown in the tables on pages 218 and 219.

NIH is still receiving well over half of the government life science funds with a current annual budget around $1.2 billion. There has been considerable criticism of NIH from many responsible authorities. Scientists who are not medical doctors seem to have an unusually difficult time obtaining NIH grants and contracts, including Nobel Prize winners. In a recent letter to the author, one of America's most honored and brilliant scientists observed:

> The situation at the NIH is very bad because it is one of a general nature. At the NIH there is no strong central authority, and it appears that the committee recommendations are automatically accepted. The committee members are individually pleasant and collectively impotent. They will readily allocate money in small chunks to a vast number of universities. The last time I made a count, 68.1% went to institutions which have representatives on the study committee, an unheard-of situation in any military research. If you go over the list of institutions which have received funds from NIH, you will see that they are almost entirely universities or hospitals. The kind

FEDERAL SUPPORT FOR MEDICAL RESEARCH, FY 1948 – 1968*
(Dollars in millions)

	1948		1953		1958		1963		1965		1966		1967		1968 est.	
	Amount	Percent	Amount	Percent	Amount	Percent	Amount	Percent	Amount	Percent	Amount	Percent	Amount	Percent	Amount	Percent
Total	50	100.0	107	100.0	279	100.0	919	100.0	1,174	100.0	1,316	100.0	1,458	100.0	1,601	100.0
AEC	13	26.0	26	24.3	37	13.3	75	8.2	85	7.2	90	6.8	96	6.6	97	6.1
Agriculture	3	6.0	6	5.6	14	5.0	23	2.5	40	3.4	45	3.4	46	3.2	46	2.9
Defense	8	16.0	23	21.5	31	11.1	88	9.6	101	8.6	119	9.0	117	8.0	114	7.1
DHEW	22	44.0	47	43.9	183	65.6	642	69.9	826	70.4	925	70.3	1,050	72.0	1,166	72.8
NIH	(17)	(34.0)	(38)	(35.5)	(160)	(57.3)	(566)	(61.6)	(715)	(60.9)	(791)	(60.1)	(803)†	(55.1)	(873)†	(54.5)
FAA	–	–	–	–	–	–	3	0.3	3	0.3	3	0.2	2	0.1	3	0.2
NASA	–	–	–	–	–	–	34	3.7	60	5.1	75	5.7	82	5.6	108	6.7
NSF	–	–	–	–	4	1.4	21	2.3	20	1.7	14	1.1	14	1.0	13	0.8
VA	3	6.0	5	4.7	10	3.6	30	3.3	37	3.2	41	3.1	45	3.1	47	2.9
Other	1	2.0	–	–	–	–	3	0.3	2	0.2	4	0.3	6	0.4	7	0.4

*Covers only medical and health-related research; such activities as research training and construction are not included.
†Excludes National Institute of Mental Health and includes Division of Environmental Health Sciences.

CONSOLIDATED NIH APPROPRIATIONS, FY 1946-1968*
(Dollars in thousands)

Activity	1946	1950	1955	1957	1960	1962	1964	1966	1967 Incl. Mental, excl. Envir.	1967 Incl. Envir., excl. Mental	1968
Total†	$3,020	$52,146	$81,268	$213,007	$430,000	$771,585	$974,454	$1,244,406	$1,412,983	$1,111,888	1,178,924
Grants	850	30,979	54,331	133,544	304,430	598,998	758,569	920,853	1,049,337	826,471	890,186
Research grants	780	14,066	33,918	89,797	202,948	433,662	529,231	604,377	681,197	598,139	642,489
Regional medical programs	–	–	–	–	–	–	–	24,000	43,000	43,000	53,900
Fellowships	45	1,448	2,562	5,397	14,570	29,080	45,786	56,330	60,123	50,990	54,991
Training grants	25	6,415	11,051	28,075	75,037	118,506	172,602	209,896	224,486	134,342	138,806
Mental health staffing	–	–	–	–	–	–	–	19,500	33,781	–	–
State control programs	–	9,050	6,800	10,275	11,875	17,750	10,950	6,750	6,750	–	–
Direct operations	2,170	15,392	26,937	49,463	95,570	137,587	159,885	217,553	257,646	229,417	253,738
Direct research	2,100	11,300	22,934	34,142	49,885	69,674	71,138	82,728	90,479	78,647	81,165
Biometry and epidemiology ‡	–	–	–	–	–	–	–	–	–	–	9,923
Collaborative studies §	–	–	–	4,668	22,142	35,857	58,060	91,460	113,445	109,726	113,037
Biologics standards	–	–	454	1,692	2,805	3,050	4,787	6,806	7,904	7,904	8,649
Prof. & tech. assistance	–	2,538	1,850	5,137	11,558	11,953	3,998	5,637	7,570	885	2,968
Training	–	171	50	251	335	475	1,465	2,107	2,319	578	1,129
Review & approval	30	803	1,049	2,789	7,076	12,799	15,171	17,330	19,903	16,448	19,433
Program direction	40	580	600	784	1,769	3,779	4,193	7,555	8,986	8,189	8,887‖
International research	–	–	–	–	–	–	1,073	1,213	3,209	3,209	3,872‖
Computer research and tech.	–	–	–	–	–	–	–	2,717	3,831	3,831	4,675
Construction grants	–	5,775	–	30,000	30,000	35,000	56,000	106,000	106,000	56,000	35,000

* Data represent appropriations, not funds obligated. †Does not include direct construction or special foreign currency program. ‡New budget category in FY 1968.
§ Data for years prior to 1962 represent chemotherapy contracts only. ‖Includes $500,000 for planning the construction of an international center.

of commercial organization which has contributed so much and so decisively to the advance of the military, space and public research is practically excluded in the NIH allocations, and the same applies to small foundations. . . . Their general policy is one which excludes risk research and practically excludes work with other than major universities or hospitals. . . . The remedy is to bring about the diversification of government health funds so as to break the monopoly which NIH now has in this field and get more funds *earmarked for biomedical research* into the hands of NASA, Federal Aviation Agency, Veterans Administration and above all, the military who know how to organize work with a push and a drive behind it and a defined goal ahead of it.

Due to the nature of the quotation above, the name of the scientist who wrote this letter cannot be disclosed.

Each government life science agency has a charter to conduct research directed at specific missions or in carefully defined branches of medicine and biology. For instance, NASA life science is restricted to life support systems for spacecraft, future lunar bases and "exobiology" (the study of life forms outside of the earth). The planetary mission life support system requirements has permitted NASA to support research aimed at inducing hibernation in astronauts. The exobiology requirement has allowed NASA to develop several unique automatic bacterial detection and identification systems to be used on Mars soft landing probes. NASA can fund a wide range of diverse medical research programs, but experimental gerontology is simply not in their charter—they cannot use their funds to support any aging study.

The Child Health and Human Development Institute of the National Institutes of Health is the only American government agency which is specifically directed to fund gerontology research. In other words, one agency has been given a monopoly on the direction and funding of all aging research. Furthermore it is a "catchall" agency which is responsible for a number of other medical areas, including childhood diseases.

NIH public relations spokesmen say that "$30 million a year is being spent on aging research." NIH grants and other expenditures are a matter of public record. Going over their lists of grants and contracts, one finds approximately 400 separate programs that could be described as gerontology studies or other aging research activities. The total funding support for all these programs is about $3 million per year. Approximately $1 million a year goes to support the NIH intramural aging research activities in the Baltimore City Hospital under the direction of Dr. Nathan W. Shock. Of the remaining $2 million, many of the grants primarily cover training and geriatrics programs, not fundamental studies of biological aging. Several leading gerontologists have carefully gone over the list of research grants, and have concluded that only about $1 million is being devoted to experimental gerontology (one-half cent annually for each American).

We have already seen that other government life science agencies cannot support aging research because it is not in their charters. An explanation of the way funds are allotted to the individual NIH institutes will complete the story of "the gerontology funding dilemma."

NIH is part of the U.S. Public Health Service (PHS), which in turn is part of the Department of Health, Education and Welfare (HEW). The way the Fiscal Year 1968 (FY68) budget evolved was typical of the pattern in recent years.

First the NIH Director, Dr. James A. Shannon, and his staff prepared a preliminary FY68 budget request of $1.6 billion and sent it to Dr. William H. Stewart, the PSH Surgeon General. There the budget request was cut to $1.5 billion and sent to the HEW Secretary (a member of the President's cabinet), where it was cut further to $1.4 billion. The NIH budget request then went to the President's Bureau of the Budget where it was trimmed to $1.2 billion before being sent to Congress in January 1967.

Congress does not deal with the NIH budget request in a

lump sum. The committees and finally the House and Senate go over the detailed appropriation of each institute. They may give more funds than requested to one institute, or give less than requested to another institute. In actual practice Congress either approves the funding requests for each institute, or gives the institute more funds than requested in the final trimmed-down budget request that comes out of the Bureau of the Budget.

In FY66, NIH received $100 million more than requested in the budget request submitted to Congress. In FY67, Congress gave NIH $65 million more than requested. Because of the severe fiscal pressures of the war in Southeast Asia, Congress may not allot any significant increases to any of the individual institutes for FY68. The National Heart Institute and the National Cancer Institute have been the branches of NIH which have been given the most sizable increases over final budget requests. One reason for this distribution is probably that a high percentage of Senators and Congressmen are in the age range where disability and death from heart disease and cancer are becoming increasingly frequent. They see a distressing number of friends, relatives, and associates afflicted by malignancy and cardiovascular disease.

The research programs of the Heart Institute and Cancer Institute have been well planned, and are deserving of additional support. There is skillful and intense competition for every portion of Federal R&D funds. The representatives of the Cancer and Heart institutes are every bit as articulate and persuasive as any of the other government scientists when they testify before the Congressional committees. Moreover, their research goals offer the possibility of better health to older legislators.

But are not Congressmen and Senators aging also? Do not they feel the vigor and virility of youth slipping away? While experimental gerontology would be of equal benefit to them, they are not told of the advances possible in controlling the aging process, but only that aging research is being funded at a sufficient level.

The official NIH attitude has been stated by Dr. Nathan W. Shock, who is also the Chief of the Gerontology Branch of the National Institute of Child Health and Human Development. Dr. Shock said in an interview published in the July 31, 1966, issue of the Los Angeles *Times:*

> If I had my way, there would be nothing done to extend longevity until we get a clean conception of what the role of the aged should be in our society.

Dr. Shock summarizes the real NIH attitude toward experimental gerontology. His own research program in Baltimore—an excellent research effort by the way—is adequately funded.

An Independent Gerontology Agency

In the past when it became painfully apparent that some important sector of science or technology development was not being adequately supported, extensive Congressional hearings usually resulted in a new agency to fill the vacuum. For example, in the late 1940's when Congress became aware that basic research was not being adequately supported by existing agencies, Senator Warren G. Magnuson and other farsighted legislators were able to bring the National Science Foundation (NSF) into existence. Without question this foundation has been one of the best-managed R&D agencies in the government and has enabled the United States to maintain its advanced position in basic research.

In 1957 we became aware of our neglect of space research. NASA was set up the following year. Despite the Soviet head start, we were able to reach a parity in overall space exploration within about seven years.

The Soviet Union also appeared to be leading in oceanology, and in 1966 the National Council on Marine Resources & Engineering Development was established to "develop, encourage, and maintain a coordinated, comprehensive, and long-range national program in marine science for the benefit of mankind." [1]

NSF and NASA are independent government agencies that report directly to the President. There is no intermediate cabinet officer and much internal politics and confusion is thereby avoided. *The only way to make optimum progress in controlling the aging process will be to establish an independent experimental gerontology agency.* Let us call this hypothetical organization the National Gerontology Agency (NGA).

When NGA is established, it should be backed by the statement of a firm national goal to control mammalian senescence. Surely this is no more unreasonable than the 1961 goal to land American astronauts on the moon before 1970—a courageous and farsighted decision by the late John F. Kennedy.

Our experience with NSF and NASA indicates that the independent NGA's approach should be successful. In fact, NSF may be supporting more actual aging research than all other government agencies combined. Aging research per se is outside of the NSF charter, but one might say that "gerontology is a state of that mind." The same scientific study might be labeled an aging study, nutritional study, cancer study, etc., depending on the investigator and the charter of the agency receiving the research proposal. NSF does have a charter to support basic research in molecular biology, to unravel the complex genetic code hidden in DNA and RNA chemistry. Much recent progress in molecular biology has been funded by NSF. NSF is probably supporting 10 to 20 times more fundamental research with a direct potential of modifying senescence than NIH.

The proposed NGA should be headed by administrators and scientists who have the same crusading zeal as the space scientists who turned science fiction into reality in less than 10 years.

Assuming that an enlightened Congress establishes NGA in the near future, what might its funding requirements be? What level of support would permit an optimum rate of progress in experimental gerontology? To arrive at the answer, let us break down one specific program into its components. The best program for these purposes is an anti-aging enzyme program based on Johan Bjorksten's cross-linking theory (Chapter 6). The same considerations would generally apply to research programs based on the somatic mutation theory, immunologic theories, or calciphylaxis. Table 1, this page breaks down the costs as they are usually presented to R&D funding agencies.

TABLE 1

ENZYME PROGRAM AT AEROSPACE INDUSTRY SALARY
AND FACILITY COST RANGES

(In Thousands of Dollars)

ADMINISTRATIVE

I	Manager/Organizer	PhD/MD	$45–$50
	a. External Coordinator: with other organizations, governmental agencies, universities, etc. Equivalent of a Corporate Staff Specialist.	MS or PhD	$30–$35
	b. Internal Coordinator: between Manager and Principal Scientists. General Research Scientist; research program organizer.	PhD	$30–$35

PRINCIPAL SCIENTISTS

II	Biochemists (2)	PhD	$14–$23
III	Organic Chemist	PhD	$18–$23
IV	Microbiologist	PhD	$18–$23
V	Clinical Investigator	MD	$18–$23
VI	Virologist (Tissue Culture)	PhD	$18–$23
VII	Biophysicist	PhD	$18–$23
VIII	Physiologist-Zoologist	PhD	$18–$23
IX	Mathematician	PhD	$18–$23
X	Creative Engineer	BS–MS	$18–$23

Each principal scientist has at least one technician-assistant in the $8–$9 range. However, the Microbiologist from the survey aspect of a part of his program will need at least two. The Biophysicist might well have two, one just for electron microscopy. The Creative Engineer could have two: a draftsman and a photographer (including photomicrography). Probably, therefore, most principal scientists will end up with two assistants.

	BS–MS	$200–$230

Continued on next page

Table 1 (continued)

XI General Support
   a. Ten Lab Assistants (outside Principal Scientist research labs)

1. Four: cleaning glassware, autoclaving, preparing triple-distilled water, etc.		$29–$34
2. Three: media and solution makers		$22–$26
3. Three: stock and supply men		$18–$22
b. One Research Librarian	MS	$10–$12
1. Two assistants/typists		$15
c. Thirteen Secretaries: one for each administrative person and Principal Scientist		$91–$117
d. Equipment Management Section		
1. General manager—senior technician		$13–$15
2. Electronics instrument technician		$12–$14
3. Mechanical and glassblowing technician		$11–$13
4. Two shop assistants		$14–$19
e. One Accountant/Purchasing		$12–$15
1. Secretary/expediter		$ 7–$10
f. Building Maintenance—Janitors (2)		$12–$14

Total Direct Labor	$733–$883
Building Lease	$ 45
First Year's Improvements	$350
Lab Equipment, Office Furniture, Shop, etc.	$800
Initial Library and Subscriptions	$200
Travel and Miscellaneous	$120

TOTAL FIRST YEAR	$2,248,000–$2,398,000

The calculations in Table 1 are for a conservative program, not the major effort that should back up a national commitment to a scientific goal. Two million dollars a year would insure some progress toward the final goal of isolating enzymes that would effectively break down cross-linked protein in our tissues. Would $20 million a year permit a tenfold increase in the rate of progress? Probably not, since there is a time factor in all biological activities. However, additional funds in a neglected research area can always be spent effectively.

The enzyme anti-aging approach deserves the highest priority, and initial success would justify the marshaling of the resources of the entire pharmaceutical industry.

The same reasoning holds for the other promising approaches to control of senescence. Once an effective anti-aging therapy is in sight, unlimited funds should be made available to permit final refinement in the shortest possible time.

An initial NGA budget of $100 million a year would probably make possible the most effective use of existing facilities. Each year $50 million could be added until the NGA budget might level off at around $500 million annually. At this point an optimum research program would be in full swing. The brightest of the young biological scientists would be encouraged to enter the field.

These estimates would amount to an initial NGA program of less than one dollar a year for each American. When it is fully developed in 10 years, it would mean little more than two dollars a year for each American. Surely these few dollars can be allotted to the control of aging, a research objective that will benefit all mankind.

17

Controlling the Aging Process

SHOULD science succeed in significantly increasing the human life-span, the socioeconomic patterns as we know them today would undergo profound change. The effects of advances in the physical and biological sciences will alter the shape of the future as much as great social and political events, perhaps even more.

Predictions of political and international patterns are of course speculative. The effects of advances in the physical and biological sciences can, however, now be foreseen with an increasing degree of accuracy. The explosive growth of our national investment in science and technology has created a need for still more accurate methods of forecasting the probable outcome of these research and development expenditures. As a result, technological forecasting methodology is being refined into a highly systematic and accurate discipline, making possible precise planning by government and industrial decision-makers.

Technological Forecasting (T/F) is "the description or prediction of a foreseeable invention, specific scientific refinement, or likely scientific discovery that promises to serve some useful function." [1] T/F attempts to forecast useful control over physical and biological phenomena beyond 10 years, in some cases up to 50 years in the future. T/F cannot forecast whether or not various technical capabilities will be exercised, only what resources will be available, and when. In some cases it outlines alternate foreseeable means of achieving a capability and points out the most likely technological option for such an achievement. By integrating T/F in planning and speculation about the future, we have the opportunity to consider in advance some of the future's technological options prior to the time they can be realized.

T/F is based on an understanding of the current limitations of science. The British Nobel Laureate Sir George Thomson has accurately defined what these limitations are: [2]

> Technology is governed by scientific principles, some of which are understood, and there is accordingly a basis for prediction. ... Developments which do not contradict known principles and which have an obvious utility will in fact be made, probably in the next hundred years. No doubt there will be discoveries which will transcend what now appear major impossibilities, but these are unpredictable, and so are the practical developments which will follow them.

Through the refinement of systematic methodologies, in the past few years, technological forecasting has become increasingly accurate. These methodologies are extensively described in my book, published in 1967, *Designing the Future, The Role of Technological Forecasting.* Advanced T/F tools are also used in answering the questions relating to the probable socioeconomic effects of longevity.

Longevity and the Malthusian Dilemma

Thomas R. Malthus (1766–1834) was an Anglican clergyman and political economist whose principal theory held that population tends to multiply faster than its means of food production. Unless population increases are checked, he theorized, poverty and starvation are inevitable. Neo-Malthusianism refers to efforts of many economists and scholars to bring

Malthus up to date. Almost all scientists are concerned with the "Malthusian dilemma": the fact that the present 3.5 billion people on earth will multiply to 7 billion by the turn of the century if the present rate of population increase is maintained —a doubling of the population in 32 years.

The Malthusian dilemma has even caused some leading gerontologists to express concern over the effects of extending the life-span. The Australian Nobel Laureate Sir Macfarlane Burnet, who first formulated the immunologic theory of aging (Chapter 9), recently commented: [3]

> Our present rate of population growth is bad enough, but if, in addition, we were all to become centenarians it would throw our whole social and economic life into disorder.

Let us first explore the possible consequences of an extended life-span on population increase. The Malthusian crisis will probably occur in the 1980 to 1990 time period and could result in mass starvation in parts of South America, Africa and in overcrowded Asian countries such as India. Even if the advanced countries could produce the food to feed these people, the transportation system within the more backward countries would not necessarily be adequate for effective distribution.

India is presently a good example of what might occur. In the 1980's, one or two years of good harvests would provide only a subsistence diet for the population. One bad harvest caused by drought, and millions of Indians face starvation. Surplus grain from the United States, Canada, and the Soviet Union can feed a few million, even tens of millions of starving Indians, but not a billion starving people scattered in remote parts of the world.

The early stages of the Malthusian crisis are already apparent. Hasan Ozbekhan is a leading American economist and long-range planner who has made a disciplined investigation of the world population crisis. He observes that "probably 12 people die every minute from starvation throughout the world today, but mostly in the undeveloped countries. This means that a minimum of 4.2 million people die per year of starvation." Ozbekhan estimates that the present rate of population growth would cause 5.1 million people to die of starvation in the mid-70's and between 6.1 and 9.2 million a year by 1985.

A Malthusian crisis in the late 1980's would force over-populated countries to adopt stringent population control measures. There are a number of advanced contraceptive methods in various research stages that will effectively meet the requirements of population control in underdeveloped countries. Still in the experimental stage is the injection that causes a woman to produce sperm-destroying antibodies for a year or longer. A pellet implanted under the skin may provide 10 to 20 years of chemical (steroid hormones) sterility. If pregnancy is desired, the pellet can be easily removed.

Technological forecasting pioneer G. Harry Stine points out: [4] "Birth control, if it is not to be a one-way ticket to national or cultural extinction, must be totally practiced by the entire world population. Otherwise, there will always be some people madly craving Lebensraum ... and it will be bloody. If a non-technically-strong people don't have birth control and go after Lebensraum (the most likely case), they will end up like the Apaches charging bravely into the Gatling guns of the U. S. Army; they will have the sheer manpower of the Golden Horde without the weapons systems of mass destruction, but they will be up against weapons systems that can negate their sheer mass of humanity. If a technically-proficient nation such as China does not institute birth control and drives for Lebensraum with advanced weapons systems, it will be equally bloody for both sides."

Population control will, of course, be necessary even if science makes no more advances in the control of disease and aging. A continuation of the present worldwide birth rate would produce a "standing-room-only" population level in

350 years. The food crisis will be reached long before successful aging research compounds the problem.

Population increases are caused by two factors: higher birth rate and people living longer. In the remaining years of the twentieth century, longevity gains will probably be only a minor contributor to population growth. Not everyone will take immediate advantage of available anti-aging measures. At first the therapies may be quite expensive. A century or more may pass before half the world's population is receiving the full benefit of all collective advances in gerontology.

Longevity is, of course, only one of the many developments that will shape society in the years to come. Automation will radically alter the pace of both industry and our daily lives. The presence of the supercomputer will probably have the greatest impact on the professional and psychological aspects of men's lives.

The multiple advances of science will make possible travel to any point on earth in less than one hour, and habitation beneath the sea. Our moods will be modified with nonhabituating mind-changing drugs. The accelerating pace of change will disrupt current social and economic order, but it will also condition society to adjust to major changes. An extended lifespan will be only one of many of these changes and one that will be the least distressing.

Education and Longevity

The educational system and the professional skills it provides are among the most important factors in maintaining a well-developed society and rapid economic growth. Perhaps the greatest advantages to be derived from extended youth and life-span will be the changes in education and increases in the total reservoir of human knowledge they will make possible.

Postwar Japan is a prototype of the situation where the proportion between population and resources undergoes sudden imbalance. In the immediate postwar years, the Japanese became painfully aware that their birth rate would soon create a severe population crisis. Their overseas empire was gone, denying Lebensraum for their increased numbers. In 1948, extensive population control measures went into effect legalizing every form of birth control. Japan immediately experienced the sharpest drop in birth rate ever recorded in a major country. The low birth rate has continued for the past 20 years. Meanwhile, the Japanese continued to invest an impressive portion of their gross national product (GNP) in education. With fewer children to educate, these funds were primarily devoted to improving the quality of instruction. Today the schools and universities in Japan are among the finest in the world.

Japan has also maintained the highest rate of economic growth of any industrial nation during the past 20 years. A low birth rate allowed more resources to be devoted to capital development and quality education of the nation's work force. A higher percentage of the population has been in the productive age range. Herman Kahn points out that in the transition period between a growing population and a stable one, "there is a net reduction for a generation or two in the proportion of dependents—and this makes capital accumulation distinctly easier."

Education is clearly an important consideration in an evaluation of extended longevity. A minimal four-year college education does not allow a person to become a contributing member of society until he is 21 or 22. He will probably retire between the ages of 65 and 70, so the ratio of years spent being educated to years productively working is about 1 to 2. Human knowledge is increasing at an ever-accelerating rate. Therefore, more years will soon be necessary to acquire an adequate education. Some authorities predict that the people of tomorrow will be students until 30. With no gains in longevity, the ratio between the education period and the working period would be reduced to about 1 to 1.

Now let us assume that today's life-span is doubled (150 years) with most of the gain being years of extended youth. Formal education could terminate at age 30. The present education-to-productivity ratio of 1 to 2 could be easily maintained with average retirement at age 90 years. Many people could work till the age of 120, an education-to-productivity ratio of 1 to 3.

The economic impact of additional life-span extensions is speculative because the details of society in the late twenty-first century, and beyond, cannot be foreseen with accuracy. Though such speculation is really science fiction, imaginative extrapolations often contain accurate forecasts.

The potential impact of extended youth on scientific research would provide perhaps the greatest economic gains, since science requires the longest period of formal education. Today most scientists are thoroughly trained in only one specialty. A 150-year life-span would make it possible for scientists to become true interdisciplinarians. They could have PhD levels of training in many specialties. Experiments lasting a century or more would be conducted by some scientists.

We do not know what the full potential of man's mental capabilities may be because senility—largely brain senescence—begins before they have been fully developed. Man's full potential will never be realized without success in experimental gerontology.

Conclusion

What is the prospect for greatly extended youth? Will it forever remain an unobtainable dream? Will massive funding allow biological barriers to be overcome just as massive funding has already permitted equally formidable barriers in the physical sciences to be conquered? The biologists who are uncertain or pessimistic should look to Arthur C. Clarke, a remarkably accurate prophet of recent achievements in science. Clarke has repeatedly pointed out that it is not the acknowledged masters of the field who can give the most reliable pointers to its future. "Too great a burden of knowledge can clog the wheels of imagination." Clarke summarized this fact in the somewhat facetious formulation of "Clarke's Law": [4]

> When a distinguished but elderly scientist states that something is possible, he is almost certainly right. When he states that something is impossible, he is very probably wrong. Perhaps the adjective "elderly" requires definition. In physics, mathematics, and astronautics it means over thirty; in the other disciplines, senile decay is sometimes postponed to the forties.

I see no reason why Clarke's Law may not be just as applicable to gerontology as it has been to astronautics, nuclear power and many branches of medicine. In the same vein as Clarke's Law, the readers may have noticed a similar fundamental truth frequently mentioned in earlier chapters:

> No theory of the cause of mammalian senescence can be completely proved or disproved without developing the corrective therapies suggested by the theory.

We will not be able to tell whether significantly extended youth may even be a remote future possibility until every research option outlined in this book, and many more not mentioned have been adequately funded and fully explored, one by one, until we have the final answers.

There have been two important scientific achievements in the past few months that would have been considered "impossible" a generation ago. The 1959 Nobel Laureate in Medicine, Dr. Arthur Kornberg, headed a team including Dr. Robert L. Sinsheimer and Dr. Mehran Goulian which achieved the test-tube synthesis of a fully infectious DNA virus in November 1967. If one considers a virus to be "alive" (and some scientists do not), then man has already created the most primitive form of life in the laboratory.

The pioneer heart transplants of Dr. Christiaan Barnard in South Africa have captured the imagination of the world. In

May, 1968, Dr. Philip Blaiberg had survived over four months with a transplanted heart and was well enough to be sent home from the hospital. Heart transplants may become routine within 5 to 10 years.

Technological forecasting pioneer Theodore J. Gordon recently wrote me suggesting that "one phenomena you might want to comment on is the tremendous popular appeal of the Kornberg virus experiments and the recent heart transplants. More interest, more news space, more personal involvement was apparent than I would have thought these events could provoke. Why?" My answer is simply that the public is vitally concerned with the anti-aging achievements of science. Their interest in the extension of the active youthful portions of the life-span has been greatly underestimated. When the full potential of experimental gerontology is fully recognized by the public, their elected representatives will demand that a major effort to control senescence be made a national goal with unlimited funding and other support.

Science cannot yet tell us how we can extend our youth and total life-span. A sparse diet may be useful. Today, a "youth cocktail" of suitable antioxidants, vitamin E, vitamin C, and a micromeasure of selenium followed by an aqueous solution of cholestryamine may add a few years. However, we could be very close to really effective anti-aging therapies. Within a 10-year period the causes of senescence may be subject to significant modification. Complete control of aging will surely be realized within the next century.

Man may gain a modest life-span extension by reducing his metabolic rate during the hours of sleep. However, other research discoveries by Loeb and Northrop are likely to be much more important in the quest for perpetual youth. Sixty years ago Jacques Loeb discovered artificial parthenogenesis, a research step which may culminate in effective cellular replacement (Chapter 12). John H. Northrop's work with crystalline enzymes in the late 1930's provided a necessary foundation for the isolation of soil bacteria enzymes that will break down cross-linked protein in human tissues.

Donald G. Carpenter and his associates may have already achieved the goal of combining all the contending aging theories into a complete explanation of senescence. Dr. Carpenter considers that Bjorksten's cross-linking theory was the greatest single advance. The anti-aging therapy proposed by Johan Bjorksten may prove to be the most important scientific achievement in human history when reduced to clinical practice. With imagination and foresight, it could be available within 10 to 15 years, ushering in the age of extended youth.

The conquest of aging is the conquest of time. It would give man the added years of youth to realize his most ambitious dreams and to achieve an education beyond the scope of any degree of learning possible today. If the conquest of senescence is the key to unlimited human knowledge, then it will also allow all of man's reasonable expectations of science to be achieved: the control of unlimited sources of energy and raw materials, the discovery and colonization of planets circling distant stars, and the transformation of our society from a pattern of war and struggle to an era of utopian peace. Most important of all, men would have adequate time to strive to uncover the secrets of the natural universe and incorporate them into a philosophy that could serve as a foundation for a civilization of never-ending progress.

Notes

CHAPTER 1

[1] Nathan W. Shock, "The Physiology of Aging," *Scientific American* (January, 1962), p. 110.

[2] Alex Comfort, *Aging: The Biology of Senescence* (London, Routledge & Kegan Paul, 1964), p. 1.

[3] Victor Cohn, *1999, Our Hopeful Future* (New York, Bobbs-Merrill, 1956), p. 151.

[4] Sir George Thomson, *The Foreseeable Future* (Cambridge, England, University Press, 1955), pp. 133–34.

CHAPTER 2

[1] Robert S. de Ropp, *Man Against Aging* (New York, St. Martin's Press, 1960), p. 170.

CHAPTER 3

[1] Robert S. de Ropp, *Man Against Aging* (New York, St. Martin's Press, 1960), p. 162.

[2] S. Braines, "Reproduction and Removal of Symptoms of Senility," *Biological Aspects of Aging,* edited by Dr. Nathan W. Shock (New York, Columbia University Press, 1962), p. 118.

CHAPTER 4

[1] Paul H. de Kruif, *Male Hormone* (New York, Harcourt, Brace 1945).

[2] Ann Walsh, *E.R.T.* (New York, Bantam Books, 1965), p. 174.

[3] Robert A. Wilson, *Feminine Forever* (New York, M. Evans and Company, 1966), pp. 16 and 18.

[4] Alex Comfort, *Aging: The Biology of Senescence* (London, Routledge & Kegan Paul, 1964), p. 251.

CHAPTER 5

[1] Gay Gaer Luce and Julius Segal, *Sleep* (New York, Coward-McCann, 1966), p. 42.

[2] *Ibid.,* p. 39.

[3] Alex Comfort, "The Causes of Aging," *Science Journal* (March, 1965), p. 71.

[4] *Ibid.*

5 *Ibid.*

6 *Ibid.*

7 Alex Comfort, private communication.

CHAPTER 6

1 Johan Bjorksten, "Recent Developments in Protein Chemistry," *Chemical Industries* 48 (June, 1941), pp. 746–51.

2 Johan Bjorksten, "Chemistry of Duplication," *Chemical Industries* 50 (January, 1942), pp. 68–72.

3 Johan Bjorksten, "Cross-linkages in Protein Chemistry," *Advances in Protein Chemistry*, Vol. 6, edited by Amon, Edsall and Bailey (New York, Academic Press, 1951), p. 343.

4 Nathan W. Shock, "Some of the Facts of Aging," in *Aging, Some Social and Biological Aspects* (Publication No. 65, Washington, D.C., American Association for the Advancement of Science, 1960), pp. 250–51.

5 Johan Bjorksten, "Aging, Present Status of Our Chemical Knowledge," *Journal of the American Geriatrics Society* (February, 1962), pp. 125–39.

6 Donald G. Carpenter, "Computer Solutions for Diffusion Theory Equations on the Accumulation of Cross-linked Molecules," *Gerontologia* 13 (1967), pp. 111–23.

7 Johan Bjorksten, "Could We Live Longer?" *New Scientist* (September, 1962), p. 554.

8 Linus Pauling, *Henry Ford Hospital Medical Bulletin* (March, 1956), p. 1.

9 John H. Northrop, "Prefatory Chapter" in *Advances in Protein Chemistry,* also reprinted in *The Excitement and Fascination of Science, Annual Review of Biochemistry,* Vol. 30 (1961), pp. 335–36.

CHAPTER 7

1 Alexander A. Bogomoletz, *The Prolongation of Life.* A Robinson Foundation Publication, Essential Books (New York, Duell, Sloan & Pearce) pp. 89 and 90.

2 *Ibid.*

3 Victor Bogomoletz, *The Secret of Keeping Young* (London, England, Arco Publications Limited, 1954), p. 141.

4 *Ibid.*, p. 47.

5 *Ibid.*, p. 142.

6 Frederic Verzár, *Scientific American* (April, 1963), p. 104.

7 Robert R. Kohn, "Aging as a Consequence of Growth Cessation," *Reproduction: Molecular, Subcellular and Cellular,* edited by Michael Locke (New York, Academic Press, 1965), p. 313.

8 Harry Sobel, "Aging and Cellular Malnutrition," *The Gerontologist* (June, 1962), pp. 85 and 86.

9 *Ibid.*, p. 87.

10 *Ibid.*

CHAPTER 8

1 Howard J. Curtis, "The Role of Somatic Mutations in Aging," *Topics in the Biology of Aging,* edited by Peter L. Krohn (New York, John Wiley & Sons, 1966), p. 64.

2 J. Maynard Smith, "Theories of Aging," *Topics in the Biology of Aging,* edited by Peter L. Krohn (New York, John Wiley & Sons, 1966), p. 10.

[3] Robert R. Kohn, "Aging as a Consequence of Growth Cessation," *Reproduction: Molecular, Subcellular and Cellular,* edited by Michael Locke (New York, Academic Press, 1965), pp. 300 and 301.

[4] Howard J. Curtis, "The Role of Somatic Mutations in Aging," *Topics in the Biology of Aging,* edited by Peter R. Krohn (New York, John Wiley & Sons, 1966), p. 74; *Biological Mechanisms of Aging* (Springfield, Illinois, Charles C. Thomas, 1966), p. 121.

[5] Howard J. Curtis, "The Possibility of Increased Longevity by the Control of Mutations," *Perspectives in Experimental Gerontology,* edited by Nathan W. Shock (Springfield, Illinois, Charles C. Thomas, 1966), p. 264.

[6] Alex Comfort, "The Causes of Aging," *Science Journal* (March, 1965), p. 75.

[7] Frederic Verzár, *Lectures on Experimental Gerontology* (Springfield, Illinois, Charles C. Thomas, 1963), pp. 112 and 113.

[8] Johan Bjorksten and Fred Andrews, "Chemical Mechanisms Underlying the Biological Mechanisms of the Aging Process," *Journal of the American Geriatrics Society* (July, 1964).

[9] Howard J. Curtis, *Biological Mechanisms of Aging* (Springfield, Illinois, Charles C. Thomas, 1966), p. 95.

[10] Howard J. Curtis, private communication.

CHAPTER 9

[1] Roy L. Walford, "The Immunologic Theory of Aging," *The Gerontologist* (December, 1964), p. 196.

[2] Roy L. Walford, "Generalized Biological Hypothesis and Aging: An Immunologic Approach," *Topics in the Biology of Aging,* edited by Peter L. Krohn (New York, Interscience Publishers, 1966), p. 166.

[3] *Ibid.,* p. 169.

[4] Roy L. Walford, "Further Considerations Toward an Immunologic Theory of Aging," *Experimental Gerontology,* Vol. 1 (1964), p. 73.

[5] Roy L. Walford, "Auto-Immunity Theories," *Perspectives in Experimental Gerontology,* edited by Nathan W. Shock (Springfield, Illinois, Charles C. Thomas, 1966), p. 354.

CHAPTER 10

[1] Norbert Wiener, *Cybernetics* (New York, John Wiley and Sons, 1948), p. 19.

[2] Joseph W. Still, "Are Organismal Aging and Death Necessarily the Result of Death of Vital Cells in the Organism? (A Cybernetic Theory of Aging)," *Medical Annals of the District of Columbia* (April, 1956), pp. 199–204; "The Physiology of Aging—A Research Approach," *Journal of the Washington Academy of Sciences* (July, 1958), pp. 224–29.

[3] Johan Bjorksten, "Aging: Present Status of Our Chemical Knowledge," *Journal of the American Geriatrics Society,* Vol. X, No. 2 (February, 1962), p. 130.

CHAPTER 11

[1] Hans Selye, *From Dream to Discovery: On Being a Scientist* (New York, McGraw-Hill, 1964), pp. 53 and 54.

[2] Hans Selye, "The Future of Aging Research," *Perspectives in Experimental Gerontology,* edited by Nathan W. Shock (Springfield, Illinois, Charles C. Thomas, 1966), pp. 377 and 378.

[3] Hans Selye, *The Stress of Life* (New York, McGraw-Hill, 1956), pp. 303 and 304.

CHAPTER 12

[1] Patrick M. McGrady, Jr., *The Youth Doctors* (New York, Coward-McCann, 1968).

[2] Paul Niehans, *Introduction to Cellular Therapy* (New York, Pageant Books, 1960), p. 9.

[3] *Ibid.*, p. 117.

[4] F. Schmid and J. Stein, eds., *Cell Research and Cellular Therapy* (Thoune, Switzerland, Ott Publishers, 1967).

[5] Gilles Lambert, *Conquest of Age: The Extraordinary Story of Dr. Paul Niehans* (New York, Rinehart & Company, 1959), pp. 143 and 144.

[6] Jean Rostand, *Can Man Be Modified?* (London, Secker & Warburg, 1959), pp. 12 and 13.

[7] A. A. Moscona, "Tissues from Dissociated Cells," *Scientific American* (1960), p. 144.

CHAPTER 13

[1] Alex Comfort, *Aging, The Biology of Senescence* (London, England, Routledge & Kegan Paul, 1964), p. 9.

[2] Jacques Loeb and John H. Northrop, "Is There a Temperature Co-efficient for the Duration of Life?" *Proc. Nat. Acad. Sc.*, 2 (1916), p. 462; John H. Northrop, "Effect of Prolongation of the Period of Growth on the Total Duration of Life," *Journal Biol. Chem.*, 32 (1917), p. 123.

[3] Robert S. de Ropp, *Man Against Aging* (New York, St. Martin's Press, 1960), p. 88 and 90.

[4] Howard J. Curtis, *Biological Mechanisms of Aging* (Springfield, Illinois, Charles C. Thomas, 1966), p. 24.

[5] Denham Harman, private communication.

CHAPTER 15

[1] William H. Masters and Virginia E. Johnson, *Human Sexual Response* (Boston, Little, Brown & Company, 1966), pp. 248, 249 and 270.

CHAPTER 16

[1] Dr. Edward Wenk, Jr., "The Role of the Federal Government in Ocean Science and Technology," *Oceanology International* (October, 1966), p. 31.

CHAPTER 17

[1] Robert W. Prehoda, *Designing the Future: The Role of Technological Forecasting* (Philadelphia, Chilton Book Company, 1967), p. 12.

[2] Sir George Thomson, *The Foreseeable Future* (Cambridge, England, University Press, 1955), p. vii.

[3] *Los Angeles Times* (July 6, 1967), Part II, p. 6.

[4] G. Harry Stine, private communication.

[5] Arthur C. Clarke, *Profiles of the Future* (New York, Harper & Row, 1962), p. 14.

Bibliography

BIRREN, JAMES E., ed., *Handbook of Aging and the Individual, Psychological and Biological Aspects.* Chicago, University of Chicago Press, 1959.

BOGOMOLETZ, ALEXANDER A., *The Prolongation of Life.* A Robinson Foundation Publication, Essential Books. New York, Duell, Sloan & Pearce, 1946.

BOGOMOLETZ, VICTOR, *The Secret of Keeping Young.* London, Arco Publications Limited, 1954.

CLARKE, ARTHUR C., *Profiles of the Future: An Inquiry into the Limits of the Possible.* New York, Harper & Row, 1962.

COHN, VICTOR, *1999, Our Hopeful Future.* Indianapolis and New York, Bobbs-Merrill, 1956.

COLE, DANDRIDGE M., *Beyond Tomorrow, The Next 50 Years in Space.* Amherst, Wisconsin, Amherst Press, 1965.

COMFORT, ALEX, *Aging: The Biology of Senescence.* London, Routledge & Kegan Paul, 1956, 1964.

———, *The Process of Aging.* A Signet Science Library Book. New York, New American Library, 1964.

———, *The Nature of Human Nature.* New York and Evanston, Harper & Row, 1966.

CURTIS, HOWARD J., *Biological Mechanisms of Aging.* Springfield, Illinois, Charles C. Thomas, 1966.

DE KRUIF, PAUL H., *Male Hormone.* New York, Harcourt, Brace, 1945.

DE ROPP, ROBERT S., *Man Against Aging.* New York, St. Martin's Press, 1960.

ENGLE, E. T., ed., *Hormones and the Aging Process.* New York, Academic Press, 1956.

FURNAS, C. C., *The Next Hundred Years.* New York, Williams and Wilkins, 1936.

GABOR, DENNIS, *Inventing the Future*. New York, Knopf, 1964.

GORDON, THEODORE J., *Ideas in Conflict*. New York, St. Martin's Press, 1966.

——, *The Future*. New York, St. Martin's Press, 1965.

GRUMAN, GERALD J., *A History of Ideas About the Prolongation of Life*. Philadelphia, American Philosophical Society, 1966.

GUILLERME, JACQUES, *Longevity*. New York, Walker, 1957.

HALACY, D. S., JR., *Cyborg—Evolution of the Superman*. New York, Harper & Row, 1965.

HEINLEIN, ROBERT A., *The Worlds of Robert A. Heinlein*. New York, Ace Books, 1966.

HELMER, OLAF, *Social Technology*. New York and London, Basic Books, 1966.

HUXLEY, ALDOUS, *Brave New World*. New York, Harper, 1932.

——, *Brave New World Revisited*. New York, Harper, 1958.

KROHN, PETER L., ed., *Topics in the Biology of Aging*. New York, Interscience Publishers, 1966.

LAMBERT, GILLES, *Conquest of Age: The Extraordinary Story of Dr. Paul Niehans*. New York and Toronto, Rinehart, 1959.

LOCKE, MICHAEL, ed., *Reproduction: Molecular, Subcellular and Cellular*. New York, Academic Press, 1965.

LUCE, GAY GAER, and SEGAL, JULIUS, *Sleep*. New York, Coward-McCann, 1966.

MASTERS, WILLIAM H., and JOHNSON, VIRGINIA E., *Human Sexual Response*. Boston: Little, Brown, 1966.

McGRADY, PATRICK M., JR., *The Youth Doctors*. New York, Coward-McCann, 1968.

MEDAWAR, PETER, *Aging: An Unsolved Problem of Biology*. London, H. K. Lewis, 1952.

METCHNIKOFF, ILYA, *The Nature of Man*. London, Heinemann, 1904.

——, *The Prolongation of Life—Optimistic Studies*. London, Heinemann, 1907.

——, *The Prolongation of Life*. London, Putnam, 1912.

NIEHANS, PAUL, *Introduction to Cellular Therapy*. New York, Pageant Books, 1960.

PREHODA, ROBERT W., *Designing the Future: The Role of Technological Forecasting*. Philadelphia, Chilton, 1967.

——, *Suspended Animation*. Philadelphia, Chilton, 1968.

ROSTAND, JEAN, *Can Man Be Modified? (Predictions of Our Biological Future)*. New York, Basic Books, 1959.

RUZIC, NEIL P., *The Case for Going to the Moon*. New York, Putnam, 1965.

SCHMECK, HAROLD M., *The Semi-Artificial Man*. New York, Walker, 1965.

SCHMID, F., and STEIN, J., eds., *Cell Research and Cellular Therapy*. Thoune, Switzerland, Ott Publishers, 1967.

SELYE, HANS, *Calciphylaxis*. Chicago, University of Chicago Press, 1962.

———, *From Dream to Discovery: On Being a Scientist*. New York, McGraw-Hill, 1964.

———, *Stress*. Montreal, Acta Inc., Medical Publishers, 1950.

———, *The Stress of Life*. New York, McGraw-Hill, 1956.

SHOCK, NATHAN W., ed., *Biological Aspects of Aging*. New York, Columbia University Press, 1962.

———, ed., *Perspectives in Experimental Gerontology*. Springfield, Illinois, Charles C. Thomas, 1966.

SHUTE, EVAN, and COLLABORATORS, *Your Heart and Vitamin E*. London, Ontario, Shute Foundation for Medical Research, 1961.

STILL, JOSEPH W., *Science and Education at the Crossroads*. Washington, D.C., Public Affairs Press, 1958.

STREHLER, BERNARD L., ed., *Advances in Gerontological Research*. Vol. 1. New York, Academic Press, 1964.

———, ed., *The Biology of Aging*. Publication No. 6. Washington, D.C., American Institute of Biological Sciences, 1960.

———, *Time, Cells and Aging*. New York, Academic Press, 1962.

THOMSON, SIR GEORGE, *The Foreseeable Future*. Cambridge, England, Cambridge University Press, 1955.

———, *The Inspiration of Science*. London, New York, and Toronto, Oxford University Press, 1961.

VERZÁR, F., *Lectures on Experimental Gerontology*. Springfield, Illinois, Charles C Thomas, 1963.

VORONOFF, SERGE, *The Conquest of Life*. New York, Brentano, 1928.

———, *Testicular Grafting from Ape to Man*. London, Brentano, 1929.

WIENER, NORBERT, *Cybernetics*. Cambridge, Mass., M.I.T. Press, 1948, 2d ed., 1961.

WILSON, ROBERT A., *Feminine Forever*. New York, M. Evans, 1960.

WOLSTENHOLME, GORDON, ed., *Man and His Future*. Boston and Toronto, Little, Brown, 1963.

Glossary

ADAPTATION ENERGY—The energy necessary to acquire and maintain adaptation, apart from caloric requirements.

AGE PIGMENTS—See Lipofuscin Age Pigments.

AGING—See Senescence.

AMINO ACIDS—The chemical molecular building blocks of larger protein molecules in the tissues. Most of the different amino acids are obtained by enzymic digestion of protein molecules. Some 19 different amino acids are known to be essential for the formation of various types of body protein.

ANACALCIPHYLAXIS—An inverse form of calciphylaxis through which the organism can protect certain organs from calcification.

ANDROGENESIS—The process in which the nucleus of an ovum is removed, and a single sperm cell supplies the genetic material. The altered cell begins to divide and grows into a complete animal. The male is the single parent.

ANTEDILUVIAN STANDARD—A life-span in excess of 900 years. Taken from the ages reported in the Bible for the ten patriarchs who lived before the flood.

ANTIOXIDANTS—Chemicals that react with and neutralize free radicals.

AXENIC ANIMALS—Germ-free animals.

BIOLOGICAL CLOCKS—Cyclic physiological responses in organisms usually in the same time pattern with some cycle in nature such as a 24-hour day, the 28-day lunar month, etc.

CALCIPHYLAXIS—A biologic mechanism through which the organism can send large amounts of calcium and phosphate selectively to certain regions (see also Anacalciphylaxis).

CHOLESTRYAMINE—A new drug which lowers cholesterol blood levels.

COLLAGEN—The fibrous protein molecules in connective tissue which are the most common form of protein in the body. It is the structural or stabilizing fiber of connective tissue. Mammalian aging is characterized by a buildup of collagen which replaces elastin and ground substance in the connective tissues and becomes cross-linked and inflexible.

CONNECTIVE TISSUE—The tissue (cells, fibers and ground substances) which binds together, connects and supports other tissues in the body.

CONTROLS—Animals in an experiment on which the experimental procedure is not performed so that they can be compared with the animals which are subject to the active part of the experiment.

CROSS-LINKAGE—The chemical process by which an organic molecule in the body becomes physically bound to another molecule.

CROSS-LINKING AGENTS—Any chemical, free-radical or energy source that causes cross-linkage or takes part in cross-linkage as the bonding source.

CYBERNETICS—The entire field of control and communication theory, whether in the machine or in the animal.

DNA (deoxyribonucleic acid)—The key molecule of life which transmits heredity and enables living things to reproduce and live. DNA molecules are giant combinations of two coiled-up, interweaving long chains. When they are pulled apart, each half contains all that is necessary to re-create the missing half and become a complete DNA molecule.

ECTOGENESIS—"Test-tube birth": a yet to be refined means of growing a mammal in an artificial environment from conception to term (time of normal birth).

ELASTIN—The fibrous protein molecules in connective tissue which gives blood vessels and other tissues the flexibility characteristic of youth. It is noncrystalline and elastic. The quantity of elastin in connective tissues decreases with age and becomes cross-linked. It is replaced with collagen which also becomes cross-linked.

EMBRYO—The stage of development after conception during which the organism develops all the organs and basic structural form that will characterize it as a member of its species. The embryonic stage in humans lasts about two months after conception.

ENDOCRINE GLANDS—Ductless glands which secrete hormones directly into the bloodstream.

ENZYMES—Soluble, colloidal, organic catalysts which control the vast majority of chemical reactions in all living organisms. Enzymes are large molecules of protein containing one or more small catalytic centers. They are sensitive to heat and acid. If the temperature becomes too high, they break down and become inactive. If the temperature becomes too low, their activity slows down or ceases. Enzymes are highly specific, catalyzing only certain reactions and not others. There are many thousands of different kinds of enzymes in the body which collectively make life possible.

FETUS (also spelled foetus)—The stage of development between the embryonic stage and birth (see Embryo).

FREE AMINO ACIDS—Individual amino acid molecules circulating in the bloodstream after being created by enzymic breakdown of food protein in the digestive system.

FREE RADICAL—An unstable molecular fragment (with free valence electrons), that last only a few thousandths of a second in the body before forming a stable chemical body with a nearby molecule, or becoming chemically stable by cross-linking two normal molecules.

GERIATRICS—The medical specialty treating the diseases most common among older people.

GERONTOLOGY—The branch of science which is concerned with the study of age changes in all living organisms. It is research, not medical treatment.

GONADOTROPINS—Hormones which stimulate the growth and function of the gonads (ovary, testis).

GROUND SUBSTANCE—A jellylike material consisting of 5 principal chemicals which surrounds the cells and fibrous protein molecules of connective tissue.

GROWTH HORMONE—See Somatotrophin.

HAHN-STRASSMANN POINT—The discovery stage in science which also makes possible an accurate forecast of the practical applications of the discovery.

HOLOGRAPHY—A process of making three-dimensional pictures using laser light sources.

HORMONES—Chemical substances released into the blood by the endocrine glands to stimulate and coordinate distant organs. Body growth, metabolism, resistance to stress, and sexual functions are largely regulated by hormones.

HYDROPONICS—The technique of growing plants in water with added chemical nutrients. Oxygen is supplied by air bubbles through the water.

HYPERBARIC CHAMBERS—High-pressure chambers where at 45 pounds per square inch there is enough oxygen dissolved in the blood plasma to supply all the body's oxygen requirements, allowing the red blood cells to be completely bypassed.

HYPOTHALAMUS—A primitive part of the brain which lies between the two large hemispheres. It is subordinate to the higher brain or cortex, but it ultimately controls the body by regulating all the endocrine glands, the autonomous nervous system and the rate of metabolism.

HYPOTHESIS—A tentative explanation or speculation how observed facts and scientific data can be brought into an intellectually satisfying relationship of cause and effect. Hypotheses are useful for directing further research, but they are not necessarily a statement of what is believed to be true. For instance, a scientist may present several hypotheses to explain experimental data only one of which may appear to him to be the most likely explanation. Before a hypothesis can evolve into a theory or law, it must be confirmed by all future research.

IMMUNOLOGIC SYSTEM—All the glands, tissues and cells which act in an interrelated process to protect the body from all foreign substances (antigens) by the production of antibodies which react with and remove the foreign substances.

ION—An atom with one or more of its outer electrons stripped off.

ISOTOPE—One of two or more forms of an element that have the same atomic number but different atomic mass. Often used loosely for "radioisotope," a radioactive element used as a labeling tracer in a molecule to detect its function in living tissue.

LANSING EFFECT—A tendency of the offspring of young mothers to live longer than the offspring of older mothers.

LIPOFUSCIN AGE PIGMENTS—A colored substance mixed with a fatty or lipoidal material which slowly accumulates in some long-lived cells such as brain neurons and heart muscle cells. Sometime they occupy between 10 and 30 percent of the volume of old cells.

LYMPHATIC SYSTEM—A circulatory system parallel with the blood system. It plays a vital role in the body's fluid balance. Lymph nodes produce some of the cells that are part of the immunological system.

LYMPHOCYTES—A variety of white blood cells which play a key role in fighting infectious bacteria by the production of antibodies which react with and remove foreign substances.

MARSUPIAL—A primitive mammal in which the young migrate to a pouch during the embryonic stage and continue their development in this enclosed area.

PARABIOSIS—The creation of artificial Siamese twins by surgically joining or grafting experimental animals side by side so that they share a common blood supply. The joined animals are called parabiots.

PARTHENOGENESIS—The process by which an ovum is stimulated into development of a complete animal without being fertilized by sperm. The female is the only parent.

PLACEBO EFFECT—A term for any harmless or neutral substance which a patient believes to be effective in the treatment of his affliction.

PLACENTA—The structure which attaches the embryo or fetus to the uterine wall of the mother in mammals. The placenta extracts nutrients and oxygen from the mother's blood and transfers these substances to the bloodstream of the growing embryo or fetus.

RADS (radiation dosage)—A measurement of the absorbed dose of energy from ionizing radiation imparted to the tissues.

RETICULO-ENDOTHELIAL SYSTEM—A group of cells in the spleen, liver, lymph nodes and bone marrow which play many vital functions including the elimination of cellular debris and infecting bacteria.

RNA (ribonucleic acid)—A giant spiraling molecule similar in structure to DNA and created by DNA molecules in the cell nucleus. Various forms of RNA produce all the enzymes and other substances which make up the tissues of the body.

ROENTGEN—A measurement of the quantity of X-ray or gamma radiation absorbed by a gaseous, liquid or solid mass.

SELENAMINO ACIDS—Amino acid molecules in which selenium has replaced the sulfur.

SENESCENCE (or the aging process)—A process of unfavorable progressive organic changes, usually correlated with the passage of time, becoming apparent after maturity in mammals, and terminating invariably in the death of the individual. Senescence has also been defined as the irreversible diminution with the passage of time of the ability of an organism or of one of its parts to adapt to its environment, manifested as diminution of its capacity to withstand the stresses to which it is subjected and culminating in the death of the organism.

SENILITY—A somewhat vague term that stands for all the physical and mental infirmities that accompany old age. In popular usage, it generally applies to failing mental processes. Mental senility is usually caused by some impairment of the blood supply to the brain, and the victims often become dogmatic, illogical, and subject to mental depressions, particularly when they fancy themselves rejected.

SOMATIC CELLS—All the cells in the body except reproductive cells (sperm and ova).

SOMATIC MUTATIONS—Changes in the DNA molecules of body cells which cause them to produce faulty RNA, or no RNA at all. This results in faulty or nonexistent enzymes and other vital molecules that are produced by the RNA molecules.

SOMATOTROPHIN (also called growth hormone)—This is a vital hormone secreted by the pituitary gland which controls body growth and is essential for proper cellular function and new protein synthesis through the life cycle.

STRESS—The sum of all nonspecific changes caused by function or damage, also defined as the rate of wear and tear in the body.

SUPEROVULATION—An altered mammalian reproduction pattern in which special hormones cause as many as 100 ova to ripen at one time.

THORACIC DUCT—An arterylike section which is the main central channel of the lymphatic system in the chest cavity of the body.

VITAMINS—Organic compounds required for normal growth and maintenance of life. Most of the vitamins must be absorbed from food.

Index

251